Date Due

A CENTURY OF PROGRESS SERIES

●

A series of volumes by well-known
scholars presenting the essential
features of those fundamental sci-
ences which are the foundation
stones of modern industry

●

A CENTURY OF PROGRESS SERIES

CHEMISTRY TRIUMPHANT

The Rise and Reign of Chemistry in a Chemical World

BY

WILLIAM J. HALE, Ph.D.

Director Organic Chemical Research
The Dow Chemical Company

Baltimore, 1932
THE WILLIAMS & WILKINS COMPANY
IN COOPERATION WITH
THE CENTURY OF PROGRESS EXPOSITION

TO
MY LITTLE DAUGHTER
RUTH ELIZABETH

CONTENTS

PREFACE

HISTORY is replete with the records of warriors and political despots. The narrative of their rise and fall is the narrative of social and economic unrest. Upon this stage of restless human activity dawned the era of scientific discovery scarcely more than four centuries ago. But mankind, more intent on incantation than on investigation, treated the early scientist with cold suspicion and ofttimes persecution.

The marshalling of the forces from the bowels of the earth—coal and water—into steam power brought on the first great world revolution. Today we are in the second world revolution; the forces from out of the heavens—nitrogen and oxygen—have been made to yield a new power.

No manner of obstacle ever can stay the march of progress. Adjustment must follow adjustment till we ourselves are in tune with nature. The ancient history of man in a totally unknown country, this chemical world; the modern history of his gradual awakening into a sphere of bewilderment some hundred years ago; and the present record of his gaining consciousness only a few years back; these in cursory form make up the major portion of our story.

The interpretations of what life holds in store for us are based upon chemical, physical, and biological principles. In a world of chemical elements and compounds, peradventure, the chemical road will not be studied in vain.

WILLIAM J. HALE.

Midland, Michigan
July 27, 1932.

CHAPTER I

CIVILIZATION AT THE CHEMICAL
THRESHOLD

M<small>ODERN</small> civilization is
the outcome of those constant strivings in man for
the betterment of his condition. From earliest day
certain decidedly fundamental forces stand out as
the guiding stars to human destiny. These forces
arose among various peoples; but recognition and
renown have followed only after the lapse of
centuries.

WRITTEN LANGUAGE,—THE SUMERIAN AND
EGYPTIAN ASCENDENCY

The first step of wandering tribes into a beginning of civilization came through introduction of
written language,—the precursor of intellectual
thought itself. There are records of early Sume-
rian and Eyptian cultures dating around 6000
B.C. The syllabic system of writing originated in
Sumeria, whereas the hieroglyphic arose in Egypt.
A hybrid form of hieroglyphic was adopted by
traders on and around the Mediterranean, and
from this latter arose the sound-sign system or

1

alphabetic form of the Phoenicians somewhat antedating 1500 B.C.

MONOTHEISM,—THE HEBREW ASCENDENCY

The Jews, during their captivity in Babylon, came in touch with manuscripts acquainting them with their own early history. By the time of their return to Jerusalem in the sixth century B.C. the Pentateuch already had been compiled. The prophets of Israel taught one God and a unified world of righteousness. Later, in fulfillment of Divine promise to them, came the Messiah to teach the Kingdom of Heaven. This contribution to mankind by Semitic people has become a guiding force of tremendous power.

PHILOSOPHIC THOUGHT,—THE GRECIAN ASCENDENCY

The Greeks, in the time of Pericles, attained the pinnacle of their glory. Under Alexander the Great the Macedonian Phalanx proved indomitable. It spread Greek influence from Adriatic to Indus. Dissolution of Alexander's army in India and his death in 323 B.C. at Babylon closed direct contact of Greece as a power with the world. Blind to their own insecurity at home, they suffered the hordes of the North to overrun the land. As a nation, the Greeks left an indelible imprint on mankind. History, philosophy, science, and language on the one hand,—sculpture and dramatics on the other; but primarily and above all else the will-to-know. And independent thinking is the greatest driving force in man.

LEGAL PROCEDURE,—THE ROMAN ASCENDENCY

The idea of world order and dominion as instituted by Alexander the Great was espoused with all vigor by the Latin tribe in Italy, later to be known as Romans. By 290 B.C. Rome was the mistress of Italy. Victory over the Carthaginians in the Punic wars settled Aryan rule in Europe.

In the Empire under the Caesars, Rome reached her grandeur,—27 B.C. to 180 A.D. Public construction was universal. Trade and luxury were the guiding motives. Labor, however, was falling more and more into the hands of slaves; and here, as in the earlier Republic, no division of gains by the wealthy was dedicated to uplifting of poorer classes. In time Italy was overrun;— Alaric the Goth taking Rome in 410 A.D. Our ancient history was thus brought to its close.

Primarily is posterity indebted to the Romans for their achievements in organization and for their code of laws. These have served as a basis for our best methods of legal procedure. In the extension of the Latin language as medium for clear and concise expression, the world has been greatly benefited. Through this tongue, Christianity itself was held together in the trying years to follow.

EXPERIMENTATION,—THE ARABIAN ASCENDENCY

The Arabs embraced the Greek system of learning. They pursued exhaustively scientific thought and experiment,—which latter the Greeks disdained ever to espouse. In the course of the Arabian overflow into Egypt and into Spain, schools of education were established. Algebra and trigonometry were developed; alcohol, glass, sulphuric, and nitric acids were discovered. The manufacture of paper was acquired through trade with the Chinese. Fertilizers for soil were introduced and the first materia medica set up.

Through the tyranny of early Christian rulers, Europe was plunged almost into barbarism. The gratitude of mankind is due these stalwart Arabians who feared neither man nor devil. The spirit of Arabian search for knowledge saved for man the best of Greek thought and supplied the leaven that was to arouse all Europe in ferment and unshackle reason in man once again.

INTELLECTUO-GENESIS,—THE SAXON ASCENDENCY

By the end of the fourteenth century the manufacture of paper had attained commercial proportions in Europe; the appearance about 1456 of the Gutenberg bible (Mainz) marking the introduction of printed books. Primarily to the circulation of books are we indebted for the overthrow of intolerant religious domination. The culminating feature here is the posting of Martin Luther's thesis in 1517 at Wittenberg. This Reformation ushered in a new period in civilization,—the rebirth of knowledge. As early as the thirteenth century Roger Bacon preached the scientific method for all things. Galileo at the close of the sixteenth century in dynamics and Newton at the close of the seventeenth century in physics were electrifying the world with scientific discovery. The intellectual horizon was widening. The voyage of Columbus, Magellan and others extended the geographical horizon. Foreign civilization contributed to upbuilding of national character at home. Monarchies of the past deteriorated primarily by reason of over indulgence of a satiated people in their own pomp and splendors. Here the emigration of select European stock to foreign colonies opened up trade on the most extensive plan.

Music, art, and architecture developed apace and redounded to the praise of these European countries. The American and French Republics at last arose through an unwillingness to submit to monarchial and religious oppression. The freedom of people was to become the outgrowth of freedom of thought, promulgated at the Reformation. This period, sometimes called the Renaissance, typifies the rebirth of intellectuality. Never again will mankind submit to religious domination. Religion must come up to man.

PHYSICO-GENESIS,—THE ENGLISH ASCENDENCY

In 1774 occurred that most far-reaching discovery by Antoine Lavoisier, in Paris, of the principle of combustion. Up to that day no one understood the nature of changes brought about in the burning of a substance (calcination) or in its reverse (reduction, the return of a metallic oxide or calx into original metal). It marks the beginning of chemistry as a science, and still more it opens the door to metallurgy and mechanical engineering. Our modern civilization cannot antedate this discovery. Some few years were yet to pass before John Dalton in 1808, in England, gave us the atomic theory as a basis for correct interpretation of chemical reactions.

The blast furnaces of the eighteenth century

acquired practical significance when they changed from charcoal to coal and coke. Rolled sheet iron was first produced in 1728 and not long afterward boring tools were capable of fashioning a cylinder from a block of iron. The invention of the steam engine by Watt in 1769 was now made possible. In the ancient and medieval world, with no knowledge of metallurgy or of accurate machining tools, we could not have expected steam power.

The substitution of steam power for man power as witnessed in the development of the steam engine, constituted the first distinct upheaval in the world's history. Between 1770 and 1779, in the field of textiles, is recorded the first inrush of mechanical inventions. In England the production of all kinds of tools and machines to serve in manufacture of machinery built up here the world's first great supply center for metals. The invention of the locomotive by Trevithick in 1804 and of the steamboat by Fulton in 1807 are outstanding events. Later in 1825 Stephenson operated the first locomotive on tracks for carrying passengers. In 1819, the S.S. Savannah crossed the Atlantic. Transportation was completely revolutionized. Even the crude steamboats of those days reduced the time of transit to about one-tenth of what it had been before—since the days of Rome and Carthage.

Certain aspects of this period point to an abrupt change,—a change which some have described as the industrial revolution. This was the change in social classes brought about by discarding hand labor for large mechanically operated units, and with corresponding cleavage between the states of employer and employee.

Man had achieved a new ability,—the production and distribution of mechanical power. This typifies the mechanical revolution: the genesis of physical science in practical form. In the years immediately following, we note an intensive study and adaptation to human needs of all types of power; heat and electricity claiming prime interest. Faraday's discovery of induced electric current in 1831 opened yet a new world. In 1835 the telegraph, invented by Morse, was an actuality.

Possibly these years following the mechanical revolution may be spoken of as the dawn-industrial era. Only two other great attainments were necessary before the actual arrival of the modern industrial era. In 1856 Bessemer invented the steel converter, making possible the production of uniform grades of steel in unlimited quantities,—the first step in "Modern Industrialism." And again by 1853 the manufacturers of Springfield rifles in this country established the system of "interchangeable-parts" for their products;— thus the second step in "Modern Industrialism."

"The Great Exhibition" at London in 1851 drew all Europe to observe the quality of its handicraft. It was the first great international exhibit in history. The success of this enterprise was measured in the intense interest created everywhere for new inventions.

CHEMICO-GENESIS,—THE GERMAN ASCENDENCY

In 1871 the Franco-Prussian War served to cement the German principalities into an Empire. This new Germany understood the value of learning. Those early detonations of individualistic thinking, reverberating from the time of the Reformation, had now become thunder peals. Scientific method was applied with all fervor to every possible industrial problem and social problem as well. Within a single decade Germany had become a world power.

In 1880 the synthetic dye industry, begun in England in 1857 and in France in 1859, was slowly being transplanted to Germany, where it was to receive such intensive study and direction. By 1886, ninety per cent of all synthetic dyes consumed in Great Britain were of German manufacture. The English and French were slow to realize the vast importance of this most fundamental of all industries the world can ever have.

Germany made tremendous strides in every branch of chemical science. Foreign students

flocked to German universities to gain instruction
in scientific method. Even the discoveries made
in other countries seemingly gained in commercial
value through German work-over and technical-
ization. This latent chemical knowledge and
power that was Germany's, loomed as a sword of
Damocles over all other nations.

The political *status quo* in Europe was threatened. This meant that henceforth Germany
should be given equal rights with other European
powers in their childish greed for world dominions. In foreign trade Germany by 1910 had
well nigh gained world supremacy. There was no
possible solution among the greedy save recourse
to war. In chemistry, Germany was far the
superior of every nation. She knew that war must
be averted till that time when synthetic ammonia
and synthetic fats were commercially possible.
By 1913 the former process was workable. By
1914 war clouds hung so heavily that the nations
were precipitated into war almost before they
realized it. The lack of sufficient fats was a great
handicap to the German populace. But of explosives there was, on the other hand, an ample
sufficiency.

Though Germany had antagonised the world,
she held all nations aloof. This primarily by
reason of her chemical prowess. Try as she could
the synthesis of fats was delayed till years after

the war. The wearing down in the morale of her soldiers and populace finally forced surrender.

The great lesson impressed upon the allies was the power of chemical industry and the complete dependence at all times of all things human upon chemical advance. Thus has chemical study come to the fore—a Chemico-Genesis of the world itself. It is the heritage which Germany gave to an advancing civilization,—the valorization of chemistry.

BIOLOGICO-GENESIS,—THE ——(?) ASCENDENCY

In the not far distant future there must come another awakening,—the dominance of another force; the birth of another star of human destiny. This is the biological development. Not alone must we become conversant with all manner of physical and chemical changes inherent in human functions but further must we attain exact knowledge and control of bacteria and enzymes in all media.

It is hoped that the agency of a war will not be required to force home the necessity of such study. Almost nine million able-bodied men had need to be killed to force the world upon a chemical basis. Nature is prodigal in her tutelage. In the insect world there would appear indeed parallels of these human devastations through mighty cataclysms that serve for racial advance.

CHAPTER II

NATURE REVEALS HERSELF[1]

Dᴜʀɪɴɢ the early days of the mechanical revolution we mark the beginning of man's scientific awakening. By the close of this revolution almost all of the common minerals had been analyzed as to chemical composition and the greater number of our ninety two elements isolated. But even yet there was no understanding as to the arrangement of atoms, as smallest chemical individuals, in building up the smallest physical individuals known as molecules. To understand nature in the larger sense man had need to understand this world of minutiae.

THE ORGANIC CHEMICAL WORLD

No event was as little heralded, nor its significance as little appraised, as that remarkable discovery by Friederich Wöhler, at Berlin in 1828; a compound known as ammonium cyanate, and of

[1] It is suggested that those unfamiliar with modern chemical terminology may find it desirable to postpone the study of Chapters II and III to a second reading.

mineral or inorganic source, was completely transformed by heat alone into urea.   Urea was known
to be the chief excretory product of most mam-
mals; its origin was attributed to some influence of
a vital force and hence it was classed as a typical
organic compound.

Now the formula of a compound is merely the
symbolic representation of the atoms or groups of
atoms (the latter called radicals) which occur in
the molecules of any substance.   With the sym-
bols for hydrogen (H), nitrogen (N), carbon (C),
and oxygen (O), the formula of ammonium cyanate
analyzed for $NCO \cdot NH_4$, indicative of the radical
called ammonium (NH_4) associated with the cyanic
radical (NCO).   Imagine the consternation in the
minds of Wöhler and his compatriot Justus von
Liebig when, by the simple agency of heat, the
atoms within this molecule were so disturbed as to
yield an entirely different compound and yet in
full possession of all of the original atoms.   Chaos
reigned.

In 1832 the Swedish chemist Berzelius came to
the rescue.   Compounds of the same relative or
molecular weights (based upon oxygen as a standard), analyzing for the same number of each
particular atom in the molecules of each compound, can only be expected to show a difference
in properties through a difference in the arrange-

ment of these atoms within the molecules. Thus ammonium cyanate, analyzing for CH_4ON_2 is here to be represented by the arrangement $NCO \cdot NH_4$; whereas urea, analyzing likewise for CH_4ON_2, is to be represented by the arrangement $NH_2 \cdot CO \cdot NH_2$. Such compounds are said to be *isomeric* (of like parts).

Furthermore, if, among isomeric compounds, the molecular weight of one is a multiple of the other they were described by Berzelius as *polymeric* (of many parts). Thus water vapor is known to have the molecular formula corresponding to the simple type H_2O. On the other hand the molecular formula for ice approaches that of three such molecules polymerized (i.e., condensed) into one as $(H_2O)_3$. Liquid water is of course a mixture.

With clarity coming into the interpretation as above, a new chemical vision appeared. Up to this time the thought of attaining by synthetic means that which arises in nature through vital forces was foreign to the human mind. It was indicative of the rise of a new knowledge. Here at last the time-worn shackles of restricted thought were broken and the chemist set free to vie with nature in the myriads of syntheses that bespeak her matchless grandeur.

THE ARCHITECTURAL CHEMICAL WORLD

Among inorganic or mineral compounds the building-up of atoms and radicals into molecular structures found early interpretation upon simple basic types, such as water (H_2O) and ammonia (NH_3). Caustic soda (NaOH), for example, is looked upon as water wherein one of the hydrogen atoms in each molecule is replaced or substituted by a sodium (Na) atom, giving rise to sodium hydr (ogen) oxide or sodium hydroxide (NaOH).

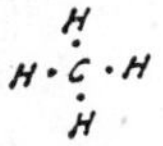

Fig. 1 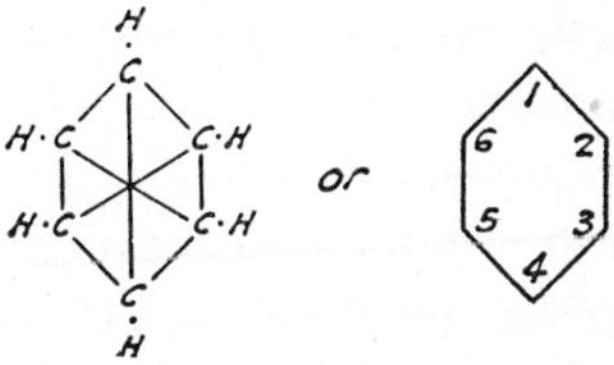   Fig. 2

In 1858 Friederich Kekulé, in Ghent, proposed the type methane, CH_4, (Fig. 1) as basis for organic compounds. It is only necessary to assume that the carbon atom possesses a combining power or valence of four as measured by its ability to hold four separate hydrogen atoms, and further, that substitution of any one of these hydrogen atoms by another atom or radical is theoretically possible if the entering group exhibits the same valence as hydrogen displaced. This simple hypothesis proved to be the key to organic chemistry now become the chemistry of the carbon compounds.

Though the Kekulé hypothesis explained well the constitutional or structural formulae for chain or *aliphatic* compounds—which commonly occur in fats and oils and petroleum—there remained a total inexplicability as to benzene. This benzene was isolated by Faraday from oil-gas in 1825 and later by A. W. Hofmann from coal-tar in 1845. It belongs to a class known as *hydrocarbons* or those compounds made up entirely of hydrogen and carbon, and is distinguished by a deficiency in hydrogen per carbon atom as seen in its formula, C_6H_6, when compared with methane, CH_4, the base of all hydrocarbons.

At last, in 1865, as Kekulé sat dreaming before an open fireplace, the curling smoke from burning embers appeared to his vision as chains and snake-like forms of gamboling carbon compounds; one figure grabbed hold of its own tail and whirled around before him—the hexagon! Like a flash, the riddle of benzene was solved.

In the benzene ring, pictured by Kekulé as a hexagon (Fig. 2), each carbon atom holds a hydrogen atom and the fourth valence is absorbed intramolecularly. Over 100,000 organic chemical compounds, of the approximately 250,000 now known, owe their structure to this and related rings; they are called *aromatic* in that many occur in odoriferous products. It matters not which one of the six hydrogen atoms in this ring may be substituted by another atom or radical the resulting compound is the same in each case; but when two hydrogen atoms in the benzene ring are substituted we meet with isomeric compounds. Thus in positions adjacent in the ring as at points 1 and 2, 2 and 3, etc., above, they are called *ortho*; once removed, as at 1 and 3, they are called *meta*; and across the ring, as at 1 and 4, 2 and 5, etc., they care called *para*.

Architecturally, the three-dimensional arrangement of atoms and radicals within the molecule was an unknown world. In the first interpretation of isomerism on a spatial plan, we owe our greatest debt to Louis Pasteur, who in 1848, in Paris, actually was able to distinguish between the closely related acids known as tartaric and racemic (found always together in the sediment of wine casks). Upon crystallization of a salt of racemic acid Pasteur now discovered two different sorts of crystals, or what are termed right- and left-handed crystals. Upon segregating these two types of crystals and dissolving the acid from each in water, he discovered that one solution turned a beam of parallel light rays to the left and the other

solution turned this same plane of light an equal
extent to the right.

Now the latter, or dextro-rotatory acid (d-tar-
taric), was found identical in every respect with
ordinary tartaric acid. But the racemic acid
mentioned above was shown to consist of an equimolecular mixture of this dextro-tartaric acid
with the new or laevo-tartaric acid, and naturally

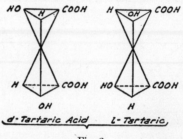

Fig. 3

any effect upon a plane of light would be neu-
tralized by reason of the optically opposing
characteristics of these two acids (Fig. 3). In
1860 Pasteur likened the structure of these two
acids to right- and left-handed screws and suggested that their difference might be explained
upon a tetrahedral structure for the molecule.

In 1874 J. Van't Hoff in Holland, elaborating
upon this spatial type of carbon atom and its
valences, showed how in methane there is *sym-*

metry as each hydrogen atom stands at the apex of a tetrahedron and the carbon atom is at the center. When, however, four different atoms or radicals are attached to this central carbon atom we have *asymmetry*, because the tetrahedral structures present now the same relation to each other as our left and right hands.

When two such tetrahedra are joined through single points, we have freedom of rotation about a

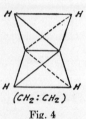

$(CH_2 : CH_2)$

Fig. 4

$(CH : CH)$

Fig. 5

common axis.   This condition obtains in tartaric acid.   When two such tetrahedra are joined along a base line the union is represented by a double bond and there is no longer a freedom of rotation; such is the compound ethylene (Fig. 4).   Furthermore, this latter state is known as *unsaturation* in that it represents a condition capable of taking up additional atoms or radicals (by the breaking of one bond in the double-bonded union) to create the saturated state exemplified by tetrahedra when

singly joined. The third possibility of union between tetrahedra is by joining of bases and is represented by a triple bond; such depicts the highly unsaturated compound acetylene (Fig. 5).

The occurrence of architectural dissimilarity within the molecules of isomeric compounds possessing carbon atoms associated with four different groups is called solid- or *stereo-isomerism*. In such relationship we find the cause for divergence in properties between the results of nature's syntheses and those of man. In the former, optical activity is more often present; whereas in the work of man, only the optically inactive prevails. Was there still a *vital force* that baffled the chemist? It is here that the biologist came to the rescue.

THE LILLIPUTIAN CHEMICAL WORLD

The "low-organism" composition of ordinary yeast had been considered since 1836. In general, the action of yeast in fermenting sugar into alcohol was described by Michael Faraday in 1835 under the head of "a catalytic force;" reference being made to discoveries two years earlier concerning the effect of metals on inducing certain reactions between gases. The *catalysis* (loosening down) of ethyl or grain alcohol, C_2H_5OH (which is the hydroxide of the organic radical ethyl,

C_2H_5) into ethyl ether and water (a dehydration process) was accomplished by a trace of sulphuric acid, H_2SO_4:

$$C_2H_5O \cdot H \atop C_2H_5 \cdot OH \longrightarrow C_2H_5 \cdot O \cdot C_2H_5 + H_2O$$

The basis of all catalysis is that the apparent composition of the catalyst employed shall not have been altered by the process in which it served.

In 1866 Pasteur published his paper on wine and there proved that in acetic and lactic acid fermentation each type of fermentation was induced by a definite species of microscopic living organism; in fact fermentation constituted a part of the life process of certain organisms. Much later (1897) the work of Buchner in Germany proved that the soluble contents of yeast cells contain the active agent capable of effecting fermentation. These are called *enzymes* (in leaven) and the particular ferment in yeast cells capable of converting grape sugar or glucose into alcohol and carbon dioxide is called zymase.

It so happens that in nature there are microorganisms which possess a right- or left-handed preference in their attack upon optically inactive or racemic compounds leaving the unattacked

free; somehow suggesting that these tiny agents—
Lilliputians of the chemical world—are grouped
into two political or really dietary sects, each sub-
sisting on what is anathema to the other.   Then
too a sort of right- and left-handed bias is displayed in plant and animal life toward building up
of compounds either of one or the other optical
activity.   Where inert particles function catalyt-
ically we may consider them the automata or robots
of the Lilliputian world.   The marvels of nature
were here just beginning to reveal themselves.

It was Liebig who, in 1840, published the first
chemical treatise on agriculture.   In this work the
nutritive values of foods were set forth.   Plant
life draws upon the atmosphere for its water,
carbon dioxide, and ammonia, while from the soil
it takes potash, soda, lime, magnesia, iron, sulphuric, nitric, phosphoric, and silicic acids.   Bar-
renness of the soil results, unless a constant re-
plenishment of soluble salts of such compounds is
made.   Hence the rise of the fertilizer industry.

In the same manner, Liebig demonstrated that
animal life requires proper proportions between
organic and mineral (inorganic) material.   Carbohydrates comprise cellulose, starch, and sugars
and are made up of carbon, hydrogen, and oxygen,
the last two almost always in the ratio of two
to one respectively or in the exact proportion as

occur in water (H_2O). Such carbohydrates are converted by animals into fats. In the presence of nitrogen compounds both plants and animals synthesize nitrogenous organic products characteristic to each type of living cell; they are known as *proteins*.

It is interesting to note that only lately has it been shown by Bertrand, in France, that in addition to the more common compounds mentioned by Liebig, living plants and animals have need of very small quantities of manganese, zinc, fluorine, iodine, and other elements.

Within the soil all classes of micro-organisms are found: bacteria, fungi, algae, yeast, and protozoa. Now when proteins come in contact with such soil, ammonia is liberated; this process of breaking down proteins is called ammonification and is accomplished by bacteria and fungi. The oxidation of ammonia to nitric acid in the soil is called nitrification and is accomplished by nitrobacter organisms. Here again, chiefly on the roots of plants, are nodules containing nodule bacteria that are capable of taking up atmospheric nitrogen (free nitrogen) directly and bringing it into combination with other elements, a process known as nitrogen fixation. The nitrates of the soil are now taken up by plant roots to form plant proteins. When the plant is eaten by animals the vegetable proteins are transformed to animal proteins, which in turn break down through animal metabolism and the waste product again reaches the soil. Thus is established the *nitrogen cycle in life*.

In the decomposition of carbonaceous (organic) matter, the fungi of the soil usually attack first and with their enzymes break down cell walls. Bacteria then rush in and convert the material to a collodial humus which other bacteria attack and convert into organic acids and finally into carbon dioxide (CO_2). The latter is taken up by the leaves of a living plant and thus the *carbon cycle in life* is completed.

The rise of chemistry during the period 1828 to about 1890 reveals a knowledge of the living grown out of inanimate matter; reveals a myriad of individual properties closely interlocked with architectural design within the molecule; and reveals an overlordship by nature herself commanding the ceaseless toil of micro-organisms as well as of infinitesimal particles of inert matter in a constant knitting and reknitting of molecules into a glorious panorama. Without these three functions earth could be naught but a ball of sand.

By 1890, some sixty years following the first revelation, we record the dawn of man's chemical awakening.

CHAPTER III

CHEMICAL INSIGHT DAWNS

Whoen at last the chemist had come upon reasonable working hypotheses concerning molecular structure in compounds, there arose a general urge to unravel the constitution of all known things.

The plant and animal world offered a myriad of entities of every sort and hue. Many of the simpler products had long been known and already had given indication of their true constitutions; but the genesis of molecular architecture in the organic world lay clouded in mystery.

LIFE'S PRIMORDIAL CHEMICAL UNIT

Since 1910 the work of Hans Fischer on haemoglobin, the red coloring matter of the blood, and the work of Richard Willstaedter on chlorophyll, the green coloring matter of the leaf, have shown these two compounds to possess closely analogous structures. An outstanding distinction however is to be found in the presence of an iron atom bound within the haemoglobin complex whereas in chlorophyll a magnesium atom is so situated.

The function of the iron atom in haemoglobin involves a union with oxygen and liberation of same for combustion of foods to evolve carbon dioxide. The function of the magnesium atom in chlorophyll involves a union with carbon dioxide and water (carbonic acid, H_2CO_3) and liberation of formaldehyde (H_2CO) and oxygen. In this latter instance the action of catalytic enzymes must be supplemented by that of light working through certain yellowish pigments.

In our organic world there is everywhere present a profusion of decomposition products of all life: carbon dioxide, water, ammonia, and mineral salts. The growing plant, through the agency of chlorophyll, is able to assimilate this carbonic acid and convert it into formaldehyde to consti- tute the first building unit in life itself. In this reaction each of the two hydroxyl groups in the carbonic acid molecule may be looked upon as having lost an oxygen atom (which is a reduction) such as to leave the remaining hydrogen atom directly attached to the carbon atom, thus giving rise to formaldehyde:

$$\begin{matrix} HO \\ \\ HO \end{matrix}\!\!\!\diagdown\!\!\!\diagup C : O \rightarrow \begin{matrix} H \\ \\ H \end{matrix}\!\!\!\diagdown\!\!\!\diagup C : O + O_2$$

carbonic acid → formaldehyde + oxygen

In the molecule of formaldehyde there is a state of unsaturation (double bond) between the oxygen

atom and the carbon atom and this is rendered all
the more sensitive by the presence of two hydrogen
atoms likewise attached to this carbon atom.
Now when a carbonyl (ie., a carbon-oxygen)
or keto group is attached to two carbon radicals
we have what is called a *ketone* as ordinary acetone
($CH_3 \cdot CO \cdot CH_3$). When however a carbonyl group
carries a hydrogen atom and is thereby possible of
attachment to only one carbon radical we have
what is called an *aldehyde* as ordinary acetaldehyde
($CH_3 \cdot CH : O$), and a more active type of compound
than a ketone. In formaldehyde we have the
carbonyl group attached to hydrogen atoms alone.
Thus this simplest possible aldehyde must display
the most pronounced of aldehydic properties.

The striking characteristic of the formaldehyde
molecule is its ability to open up or dissociate a
molecule of water into hydrogen and hydroxyl
groups (called ions) and to attach these dis-
membered groups directly to itself through the
opening of one of its bonds (of unsaturation);
the hydrogen is taken up by the oxygen and the
hydroxyl by the carbon. The result is dihydroxy-
methane, which is the simplest dihydric alcohol:

$$\begin{array}{ccc}
\overset{H}{\underset{H}{>}}C : O + H_2O \rightarrow & \overset{H}{\underset{H}{>}}C{-}O + H{-}{-}OH \rightarrow & \overset{H}{\underset{H}{>}}C\overset{OH}{\underset{OH}{<}}
\end{array}$$

The remarkable propensity of this hydrated formaldehyde molecule to associate with yet another molecule of itself, through accompanying loss of one molecule of water between the two, makes for a building up (called condensation) of carbon chain compounds. Traces of mineral salts in aqueous solution supply the proper media. At this point all life begins.

CONDENSATION

When formaldehyde now enters upon its life building mission in this world, the primary stages of its condensations comprise three- and five- and six-membered carbon chains (Fig. 6). These condensation products are both alcohols (hydroxylated hydrocarbons) and aldehydes or ketones (depending upon position of carbonyl group). They are invariably sweet to the taste and are known as sugars, and all belong to the great class of carbohydrates. Up to the time of this interpretation of condensation between molecules of formaldehyde nothing was known of synthetic steps in life processes.

The first synthetic sugar, known as α-acrose, was produced in 1887 by Emil Fischer in Germany; and in accordance with the steps indicated (Fig. 6). It proved to be optically inactive but its laevo-rotatory form is well known in nature as

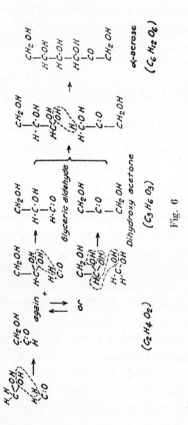

Fig. 6

fruit sugar or levulose (called also d-fructose).
Fischer's beautiful transformation of grape sugar
or glucose into fructose and back again stands out
as the greatest masterpiece in all chemistry prior
to this century.

In nature the five and six carbon sugars make
up the great portion of the first or "sugar group"
of carbohydrates. They are called *monosac-
charides* or simple sugars. Their tendency, through
addition and then elimination of a molecule of
water, to assume ring structure is depicted in the
formula here given for glucose (Fig. 7) and in those
for fructose (Figs. 8 and 9); the last constituting
the so-called γ-fructose. When once these monosaccharide rings come into play in living matter we
enter upon the most complicated and yet the most
fascinating field in chemistry.

The union of two molecules of a monosaccharide
into a *disaccharide* is accomplished through an
oxygen atom tie introduced by the abstraction of
a molecule of water from a pair of hydroxyl groups,
one in each sugar; the oxygen atom thus left as the
bridge between the two sugars is described as the
anhydride (without water) tie. Upon again taking
up a molecule of water at this point two hydroxyl
groups, one for each simple sugar molecule, replace
this oxygen tie and the disaccharide is said to be
hydrolyzed.

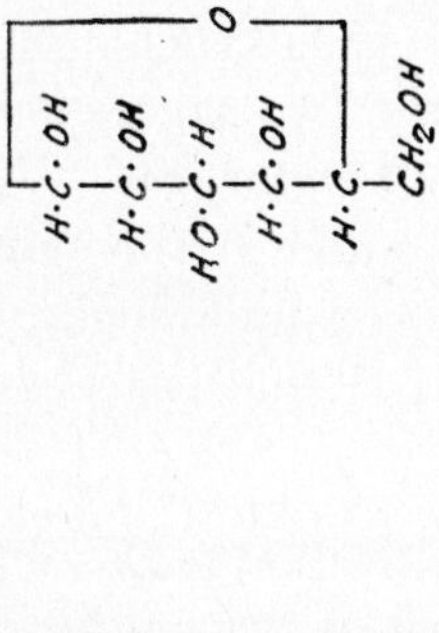

d-Glucose
Fig. 7

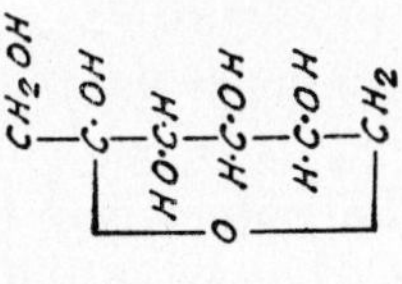

d-Fructose
Fig. 8

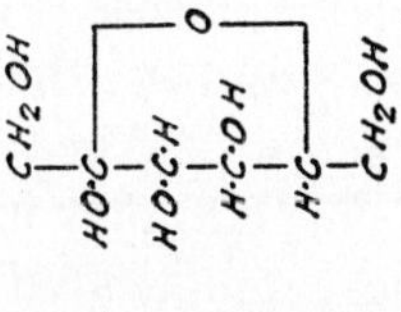

γ-Fructose
Fig. 9

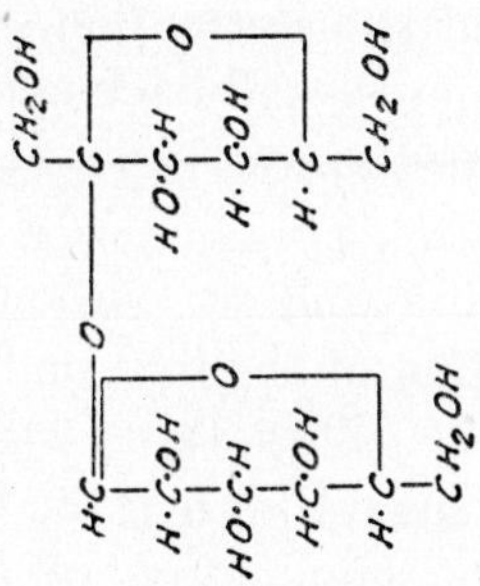

Sucrose
Fig. 10

Cane or beet sugar is a disaccharide (Fig. 10). This particular sugar readily takes up a molecule of water and is hydrolyzed (as in the human system) into its original members, d-glucose and γ-fructose, but the latter is so unstable that it immediately rearranges itself into the stable d-fructose. The molecular structures for many of the sugars, as established through researches of Irvine, Haworth, Freudenberg, Hudson and others within the past twenty years, constitute indeed the basis of a new science—the chemistry of life.

The great preponderance of glucose and the simple sugars in cell sap makes for a pronounced tendency for such sugars to enter into condensation with other compounds likewise arising in plant growth. Notably among these latter are the hydroxyl derivatives of aliphatic compounds (called alcohols) or of aromatic compounds (called phenols). The resulting products are known as *glucosides*. When two molecules of glucose condense end-on with one molecule of glyceric aldehyde (Fig. 6) a long chain of fifteen carbon atoms comes into play. By dehydration steps this is transformed into a three-ring type of compound representative of the structure of the most abundant of all plant pigments—the anthocyanins. Light itself is an important factor in bringing about anthocyanin formation in vegetables and fruits;

apples, for example, do not take on a red color in darkness.

To this class of pigment, soluble in the sap of flowers, do we owe much of the beautiful coloring in nature. In oxidized form, known then as flavones, this material becomes insoluble and makes up much of the yellow and orange in plant tissues. Depending upon condition of sap especially toward the borders of flower petals, where concentration is higher, the anthocyanins reveal themselves in a wonderful display of gradation to deeper tints. Throughout the plant world the mechanism involved in the production of multiplicity of color is surpassingly simple; it commands the admiration of every chemist.

POLYMERIZATION

In the condensation of formaldehyde with itself we may come upon forked chain structures and notably here is the unsaturated five carbon chain isoprene $CH_2 : C(CH_3) \cdot CH : CH_2$. Compounds of this type polymerize readily to give a number of hydrocarbons known as *terpenes*, $(C_5H_8)_n$, which make up the essential oils found in sap and tissues of many plants. Among their oxygen derivatives of ring type are menthol and camphor.

When the polymerization of isoprene has proceeded to superior extent in chains we call the product a super polymer; it is known by the name of *indiarubber* and is supposed to exist in spiral form. The action of sulphur in setting such structure is known as vulcanization.

In the reaction of ammonia (NH_3) upon certain formaldehyde condensations we come upon the highly polymerized *proteins*,—the nitrogenous components of living cells. The complexity of a protein is evidenced in the molecular weight of over 34,000 for egg albumin.

The first step in dehydration of a simple sugar has been shown to yield a disaccharide. The union of many molecules of a simple sugar may be instituted through the abstraction of a molecule of water between each adjoining pair of sugar molecules in the chain and thus yield a *polysaccharide*. This, of course, is equivalent to the removal of one molecule of water per each molecule of simple sugar. The formula $C_6H_{12}O_6$ then becomes $C_6H_{10}O_5$; which in polymerized form is expressed as $(C_6H_{10}O_5)_n$.

The polysaccharides constitute the second and more extensive groups of carbohydrates; such are described as the "non-sugars." Among these are inulin (made up of units of fructose anhydride), starch and glycogen (made up of units of glucose anhydride) and cellulose (also made up of units of glucose anhydride but in alternate configuration).

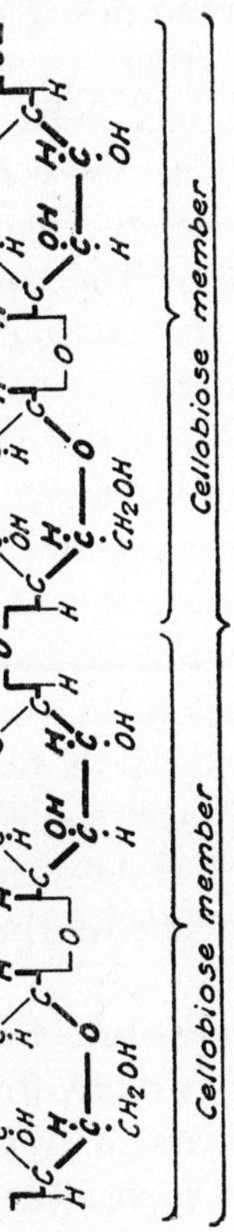

Fig. 11

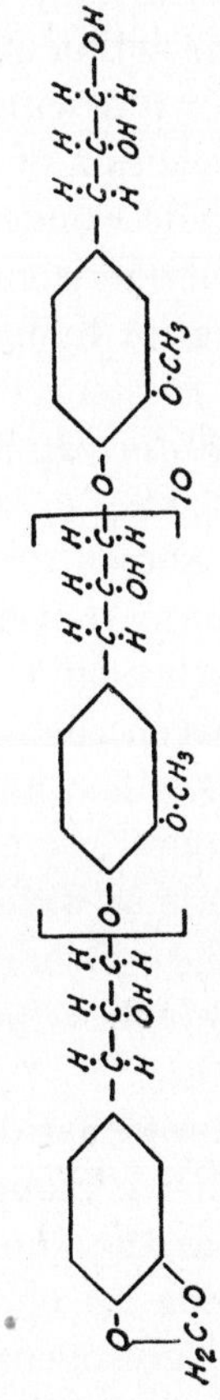

Fig. 12

Cellulose under x-rays shows crystalline structure. Upon partial hydrolysis cellulose is shown by Meyer and Mark and Hess and Pringsheim to yield cellobiose (Fig. 11) which is a dehydrated form (i.e., anhydride) of d-glucose. A bale of fifty or more chains in each of which are one or two hundred glucose units linked as in cellobiose constitutes the micelle or smallest morphological unit of cellulose. This micelle may contain 5,000 glucose units. In the space formula here given for cellulose the heavy shading marks front position.

In the formation of lignin, the encrusting material to plant cell growth, we have virtually a glucoside. The formula for a polymer of twelve units is here given (Fig. 12), but all hydroxyl groups in the aromatic nucleus are shown as methylated which in fact is the effect of the ever present formaldehyde.

In recent years H. Staudinger and co-workers in Germany have succeeded in synthesizing compounds of a molecular weight as high as 300,000. Among these super polymers, textile properties are found to appear at a point of about 8,000 in molecular weight, indicating that these exceeding long molecules (macromolecules), in bundles or micelles, are further assembled into fibrils of which textile fibres consist.

At last polymerization is seen in its true light.

It is nature's method of attaining structural
security in her handiwork. By no means are the
possibilities exhausted. By man's help she can
build far greater than mortal man dare to dream.

DEGRADATION

In nature, amid the ever present influence that
leads to condensations and resultant polymeriza-
tions, there is likewise a destructive agency that
operates to tear down the structures so beautifully
and wonderfully formed. Dehydrating and hy-
drating enzymes function here to such ends and
the broken down structures are known as degradation products. The metabolism of foods
proceeds similarly.

By such agencies we account for the splitting of
ring structures of carbohydrates and shifting of
hydrogen atoms to one end of chain and oxygen to
the other eventuating in the well-known fatty
acids as may be illustrated in stearic acid,
$CH_3(CH_2)_{16} \cdot COOH$, and oleic acid, $CH_3(CH_2)_7 \cdot$
$CH:CH \cdot (CH_2)_7:COOH$; the latter still possessing
one unsaturation. Now the tendency for all acids
in living organisms to seek neutrality is registered
in the esterification (salt formation) of these acids
by the conjointly occurring trihydric alcohol
glycerol $(CH_2OH \cdot CHOH \cdot CH_2OH)$, resulting in

fats and oils which are triglycerides of varying
proportions yet mainly of these two acids.

The amino (NH_2) derivatives of simple sugars
may be broken down and rearranged in various

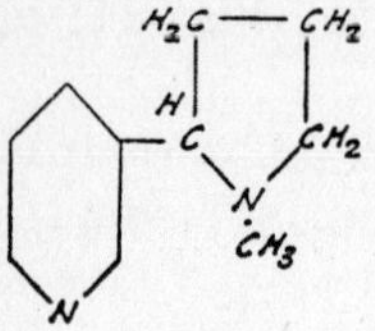

Fig. 13

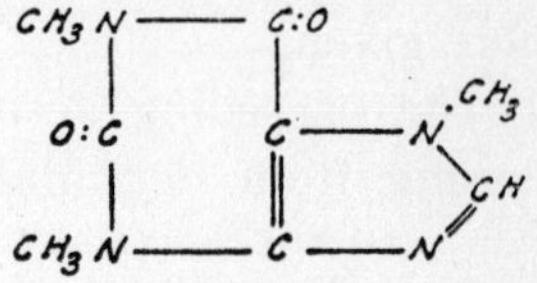

Fig. 14

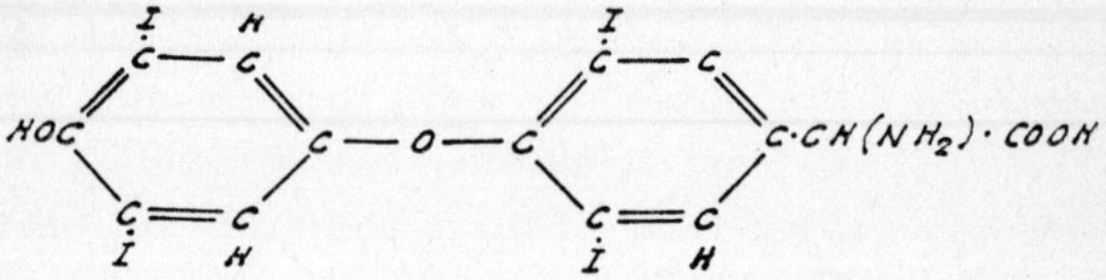

Fig. 15

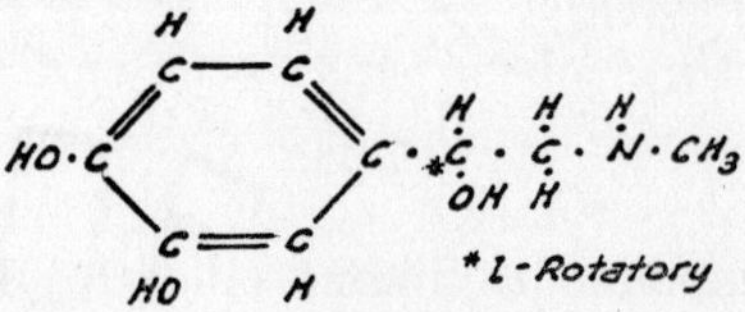

Fig. 16

ways. When one nitrogen group is brought thus
into the corporate structure of a ring containing
five additional carbon atoms we call the ring
pyridine; if there are but four additional carbon
atoms we call the ring pyrrole.

Most all of the alkaloids are built upon the pyridine ring, though some of the most poisonous are built upon this ring nuclearly condensed with benzene. As illustrations the structural formulae for nicotine (Fig. 13) and caffeine (Fig. 14) are here given.

The exceeding activity of certain derivatives arising from degradation products is witnessed

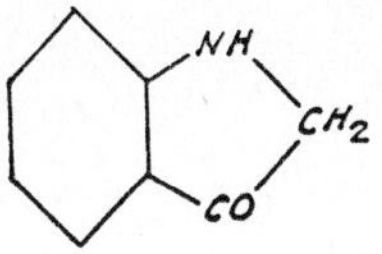

Fig. 17

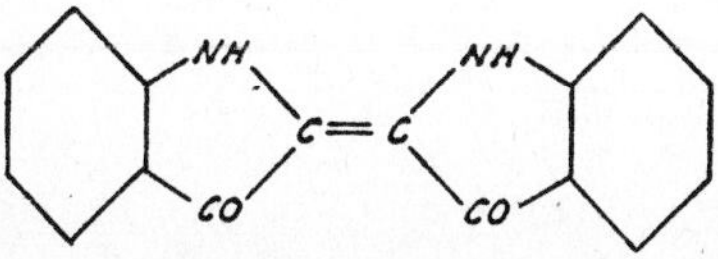

Fig. 18

in the compound thyroxine (Fig. 15) the iodine carrier in the thyroid gland. This was isolated in 1915 by E. C. Kendall in this country and synthesized in 1926 by C. R. Harington in England. Somewhat akin to this *hormone* (bodily function regulator) is the product from the adrenal glands called adrenaline (Fig. 16), isolated and studied by John Abel of Johns Hopkins University.

Among the naturally occurring dyes the formation of the degradation product indoxyl (Fig. 17) within the plant and its immediate coupling with ordinary glucose gives the glucoside called indican which occurs as such in *indigoferrae tinctoria*. Indigotine or *indigo* (Fig. 18) is the blue coloring matter that results upon oxidation and condensation of two molecules of indoxyl; it was synthesized in 1878 by Adolph von Baeyer in Germany. Occurring with indigotine, in extracted mass of crude plant, is also a reddish dye (indirubin) an isomer of the indigotine.

WATER THE WONDER-WORKER

Chief of all requisites in plant and animal growth is water. Normal development here can proceed only through a generous water supply to insure the proper intake of carbon dioxide. Upon genesis of the primordial formaldehyde water assumes directive control. By water the formaldehyde molecules are spun into chains and rings; by water these simpler compounds are condensed into fabric and polymerized into the structure of living matter; by water the whole is degraded to supply a multitude of products that are required in the orderly functioning of an organic world; and in the end, when the course of life is run, water oxidizes all back into carbon dioxide for a renewal of the cycle. In the inorganic world water similarly plays the all important rôle in the cementation and disintegration of matter.

In plant growth a sufficiency of water favors hydrolysis of starch to soluble sugars capable of acting as pressure pumps in transporting building material to plant extremities. A deficiency of water favors starch formation and excessive concentration of cell sap such as materially inactivates the enzymes. Thus the decline in photosynthetic activity in plants is a result of water shortage.

On a hot summer day a good sized leaf, as that of the sunflower, can accomplish an equivalent of photosynthesis as measured by the intake of four cubic centimeters (one thimble full) of carbon dioxide per hour. The chemical reaction is carried on within the chloroplasts—those tiny structures within the cells that hold the chlorophyll and other pigments and starch. The wave length of light preferred is that permitted to pass through the anthocyanins and flavones; usually a light in the red portion of the spectrum.

EQUILIBRIA

By the close of the past century many of the factors that determine the course and velocity of chemical reactions had become fairly well understood. All manner of equilibria attracted closest attention and scrutiny. As we look back upon this period we marvel at the centering of chemical activities upon a *fossil world;* witness for example the researches upon minerals and the advances heralded in dyes and pharmaceutical compounds emanating from coal-tar.

On the other hand, nature's laboratory offered an amazing assortment of compounds which were just beginning to reveal their marvellous designs in molecular architecture; it was the dawn of chemical insight. However a rational interpretation of equilibrial relations governing nature's synthetic processes was practically unknown. Thus we are brought face to face with the chemistry of the immediate present and the future. This is the chemistry of a *living world*. All that has gone before—even down to the close of the great war, is as child's play to the real chemical studies before us. Without an increasing intimate knowledge of life processes there can be no further advance for mankind.

Not until 1903 do we find the experimental evidence by Croft Hill actually demonstrating that enzyme action is reversible. When, for example, glucose is in high concentration in solution the same enzyme that leads to its dehydration into a disaccharide will, on the other hand, in dilute solution hydrolyze this disaccharide back into glucose.

Now the glucosides in nature always occur along with the particular enzymes that are capable of hydrolyzing such glucosides back into original members. In other words the continuation of life is dependent upon enzyme action in forcing a shift in equilibria within chemical media toward the side of molecular aggregation (building up). These enzymes to some extent are housed by the glucosides; possibly they are individual glucoside molecular units in close association with protein or other material but presenting the distinctive or specifically constituted surface which can function as catalyst toward bringing together additional members requisite for the glucoside synthesis. The close similarity in configurations between the catalytic home and the substances to be affected has been pointed out by Hugh Taylor of Princeton University in his discussions of so-called extra-lattice architecture. Furthermore it must not be forgotten that in living organisms these very glucosides are capable of replenishing the enzymes themselves when the concentration of the latter becomes too low.

In 1912 Sir Frederick Hopkins in Cambridge, England, demonstrated the inability of animals to live on proteins, carbohydrates, fats and mineral salts alone. A slight amount of milk (4 per cent of total solids consumed) when added to these ingredients rendered the diet complete. These additional compounds here required for a normal diet were found to be of several types, but all are known as *vitamines*. They are organic in structure; already several have been isolated. They no doubt bear a close genetic relationship with the hormones aforementioned, which, taken up by the blood in minutest quantity, produce remarkable effects upon regulation of bodily functions. Thus we have come upon another domain of catalytic agents that make for the shift in chemical equilibria toward the continuation of life.

From an entirely different angle we are made aware that atomic integration and disintegration, with its concomitant emission of radiant energy in various degrees, has operated abundantly to the building up of correspondingly wider ranges of highly polymerized structures. To this is accredited the rise of such great diversity in living species during the early days of life on this planet.

And thus the complexities are unravelling, but the patient and incessant toil of countless investigators is required in the task. There are no ends to the problems and never can be, but each step forward opens a wee bit more of the beauties the cosmos holds.

CHAPTER IV

INDUSTRIALIZATION BROADENS

Industry in general comprehends four basic activities—mining, agriculture, manufacture, and transportation. Pertinent to the advance in civilization following the mechanical revolution, it becomes now our duty to trace the influence of chemical discovery on industrialization.

There was no chemical enterprise of industrial significance prior to the advent of Leblanc's soda process, originated in 1787 and under operation in Paris a few years thereafter. Somewhat later we note the beginnings of commercial manufacture of sulphuric and of nitric acids.

DYES

In 1856 occurred a discovery of far-reaching import. Sir William Henry Perkin, working in the laboratory of A. W. Hofmann then a professor at the Royal College of Chemistry in London (1845–1865), accidentally discovered among the oxidation products of aniline with chromic acid a compound exhibiting tinctorial properties. It was the first synthetic dye. Within a year (1857) a small plant was built by Perkin at Greenford Green and this violet dye under the name of *mauve* at once entered commercial production.

The starting point for this dye was aniline ($C_6H_5NH_2$) which is the amino (NH_2) derivative of benzene; aniline was prepared by reduction of the nitro (NO_2) derivative of benzene arising by action of nitric acid (HNO_3) upon benzene itself. These manufacturing steps were fraught with

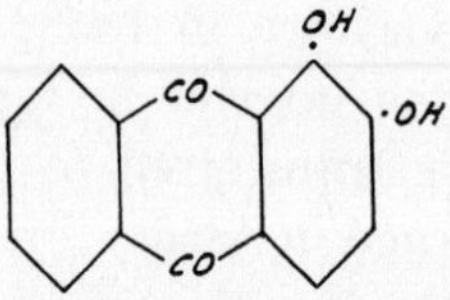

Fig. 19

difficulties and expense. Anything like chemical control was unknown; thus by a mere shift in oxidizing agent upon crude aniline a red dye known as *magenta* made its appearance. This latter was placed in commercial production in 1859 at Lyons, France.

In 1868 the German chemists Graebe and Liebermann, starting with anthracene (a hydrocarbon isolated from coal-tar), were able to synthesize a naturally occurring dye known as *alizarin*, which when precipitated on fibre is called *turkey red*. This dye (Fig. 19) was then obtained from the roots of the madder plant. By 1869 Perkin had introduced a commercial process for its production at Greenford Green. Thus the chemist was brought directly in conflict with one of the oldest of agricultural pursuits; this dye was used by the ancient Egyptians on mummy cloths.

Still another class of dyes called azo dyes, by reason of their containing a pair of nitrogen (called azote in French) atoms, was discovered in Hofmann's laboratory in 1858 by Peter Griess. But this growing interest in synthetic chemistry was soon to be transferred to Germany whither Hofmann returned in 1865. From this latter date to 1874 there was not even a professorship in organic chemistry in all England. No instance of such extreme stupidity on the part of any two nations has ever been recorded in the history of the world as when France and England gave up the dye industry to Germany.

By 1880 the dye industry, under German tutelage, was rapidly gaining recognition. The uninviting coal-tar distillates constituted the source of its various hydrocarbon starting points. By constant and laborious study chemists were soon in command of a wide range of color production.

At about this time von Baeyer's unravelling of

the constitution of indigotine (indigo) turned everyone's attention to its possible manufacture. Indeed this may be described as the goal of goals among early chemists. Even after Heumann's discovery in 1890 of the phenyl glycine process (as in use today) seven more years were required before actual manufacture became feasible; October, 1897 marks the date when this king of the dyes first entered commercial production.

The reasons for such delay were not far to seek. The state of manufacturing art was low. In the process under question a concentrated sulphuric acid (H_2SO_4), an abundance of chlorine (Cl), and a strong caustic soda liquor (NaOH) were absolutely necessary—to say nothing of the organic chemicals involved. Now these prerequisites were simply unattainable in quantity. Not till 1901 can the Knietsch contact sulphuric acid process be described as having attained practicability.

Before 1890 there was absolutely no appreciable supply of chlorine in the world. In that year the Griesheim diaphragm cell, applicable to aqueous salt solutions, was placed in actual operation. Its development paved the way for indigo. In this cell an aqueous sodium chloride solution was decomposed by means of an electric current, yielding chlorine at one electrode and a solution of caustic soda at the other. Though caustic

soda and soda itself (Na_2CO_3) had long been pro-
curable this new type of cell, and others following,
have all but made the electrolytic chlorine-caustic
process supreme.

This urge to attain the indigo victory so long in
the making—over nineteen years since its first
laboratory synthesis, raised the state of chemical

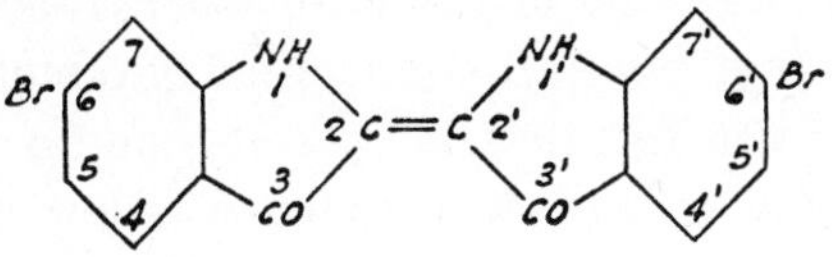

Fig. 20

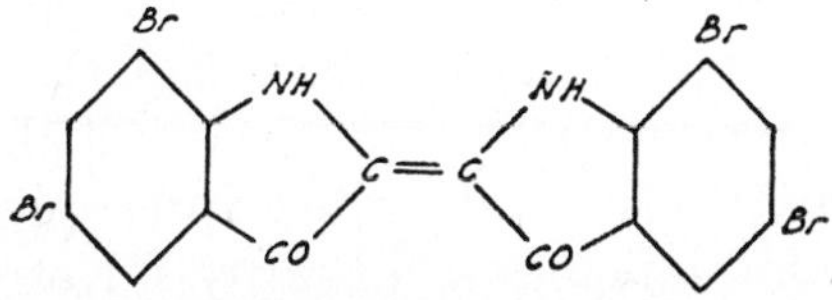

Fig. 21

knowledge everywhere and pointed to better
control in all industry. It was not long before
the indigo chemist sought even to better his
product beyond that provided by nature through
many milleniums. In 1909 Friedlaender synthesized 6, 6'-dibromindigotine (Fig. 20) and found it
identical with Tyrian purple of the ancients;
over 12,000 molluscs (murex brandaris) were
collected on Italian shores to yield 1.4 grams of

this dye to confirm his research. And today we brominate indigo directly to a number of valuable fast dyes, notably among which is a tetrabrom indigo (Ciba Blue 2B) (Fig. 21) far superior to the ancient Tyrian purple of similar constitution.

Again in 1905 Friedlaender discovered the beautiful red thioindigo, a direct counterpart of indigotine wherein the imino (NH) groups of the latter are replaced by sulphur (thio) atoms. Insight into indigotine structure led to amplification in new ranges of color. In general these indigoid dyes constitute our first vat dyes; dyes that are capable of reduction to a soluble leuco or colorless base in "vats" or tubs, and from which solutions the immersed textiles absorb the colorless base to be dyed (i.e., impregnated with the original insoluble dye) immediately that they are exposed to the oxidizing action of air. In 1901 R. Bohn discovered another type of vat dye called indanthrene (Fig. 22). In brilliance and fastness to light it has few competitors. Furthermore by halogenation this fastness is enhanced. Possibly no class of dyes has attracted more attention of late than certain of the azo colors; they lend themselves most admirably to development upon the newer silks. An illustration of such is given in the formula of variamine blue (Fig. 23).

We should not forget that discovery is far

ahead of practice.   We now know the constitution
of many naturally occurring compounds for which
we have no adequately serviceable manufacturing
steps.   Perhaps they will continue to be procured
direct from nature.   We may mention the dye
curcumin (from turmeric) used in foods; the dye

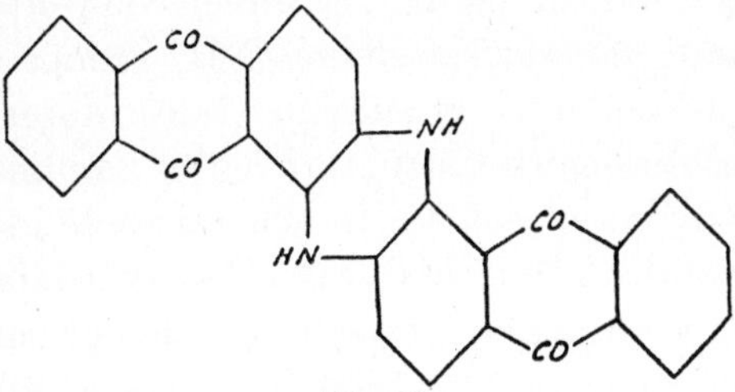

Fig. 22

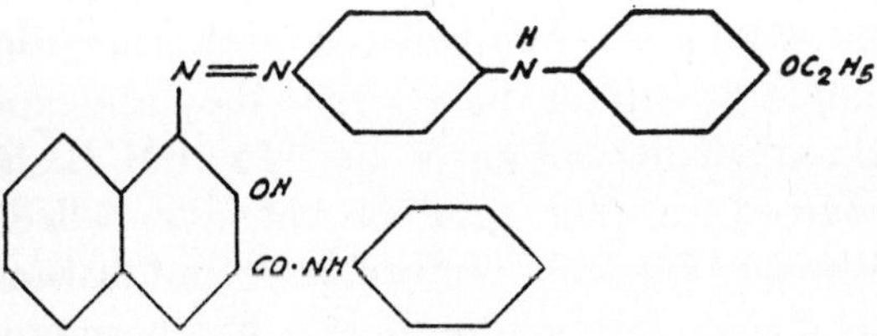

Fig. 23

haematein (from logwood) used on silk; and the
interesting but complex insecticide rotenone (from
derris root).

HALOGEN COMPOUNDS

As the dye industry grew so also grew the inter-
related industries.   The chlorine industry opened

up a tremendous field in direct bleaching, water purification, and in halogenation of organic compounds. Carbon tetrachloride was the first of these to find use in this country. Recently, it has been recognized as the supreme, non-flammable, dry-cleaning agent; it possesses an admirable selective solvent power for foreign matter with little or no destructive action upon fibres.

The commercial production of the other halogens was only a matter of time. Bromine, iodine, and fluorine are all now in steady demand. Ethylene bromide ($BrCH_2 \cdot CH_2Br$) finds a large use together with lead tetraethyl ($Pb(C_2H_5)_4$) in making up the "Ethyl fluid" going into Ethyl gasoline. Bromides and iodides are indispensable to photography and medicine. Iodine is now in production direct from our southern and western brines. Of the 350 or more tons consumed annually in this country, all should find its origin here within two years more. Fluorine is entering the household refrigerator industry by way of a carbon dichlor-difluoride.

The introduction of a great number of halogen-substituted hydrocarbons followed in the wake of carbon tetrachloride and chloroform (its reduction product). From another direction the interaction of lime and coke gave calcium carbide (CaC_2) which upon treatment with water gave off acetylene (C_2H_2). This unsaturated hydrocarbon led to acetylene halides and especially trichlorethylene ($ClCH = CCl_2$).

Still again the cracking of petroleum affords a number of hydrocarbons just now coming into considerable use:—Ethylene, propylene, the butylenes and the amylenes, as well as their saturated counterparts,—ethane, propane, the butanes, and the pentanes, together with methane, of course. From ethylene by action of chlorine and water, we come to ethylene chlorohydrin ($ClCH_2 \cdot CH_2OH$) the source of glycol ($HOCH_2 \cdot CH_2OH$); the ethers and esters of this glycol afford a valuable set of solvents notably among which is cellosolve.

AMMONIA

In 1895 Frank and Caro succeeded in preparing calcium cyanide and cyanamide by direct union of nitrogen with calcium carbide. In 1905 a small plant was constructed in Germany to produce calcium cyanamide as a fertilizer and as a source of ammonia. The arc process of producing nitric oxides direct from air was under simultaneous development but costs proved prohibitive.

The commercial synthesis of ammonia direct from nitrogen and hydrogen was an accomplished fact in 1913. This Haber process made possible a cheap nitric acid through the direct oxidation of ammonia (Ostwald process). As nitric acid attained reasonable costs, the utilization of dyes originating in aniline (from nitrobenzene) became more and more extended. The synthesis of aniline by direct ammonolysis of chlorobenzene under moderately high pressure and temperature (Hale-Britton process) has now thrown the antequated reduction process of Perkin's days into the discard.

HYDROXYL COMPOUNDS

The growing demand for solvents was much accentuated during the World War. The manufacturers of smokeless powder encountered a shortage in acetone. The Fernbach process for a specific fermentation of starch into acetone and butyl alcohol was immediately attempted. To-day in this country an abundance of these two solvents arises through this process; butyl alcohol and its esters are highly prized in the lacquer industry. Ethyl alcohol results in a small way in this butyl alcohol production; the main source, however, for ethyl alcohol is the fermentation of black strap molasses and glucose (dextrose).

Another type of fermentation is that introduced by Arthur Buswell of the University of Illinois to make use of sewage in connection with waste cellulosic matter, whereby only methane and carbon dioxide are evolved.   City sewage may soon be at a premium.   Already in successful commercial production are glycerol, citric, and lactic acid by fermentation processes applied to sugar.

Ethyl acetate is the king of esters in the lacquer industry.   Synthetic production of ethyl alcohol direct from ethylene is now carried out but here the competition with ethyl alcohol from fermentation sources is delicately balanced.   It is not likely that the synthetic process will be allowed to gain control; and rightly so in that agricultural sources must ever be encouraged.

HYDROGENATION

The interesting development in catalysts that led to the hydrogenation of nitrogen naturally incited the interest of those concerned with carbon.   From 1897 to 1914 Paul Sabatier and his co-workers in France opened a vast storehouse of catalytic possibilities.   Sabatier discovered that finely divided nickel and other agents were capable of effecting a union between hydrogen and any number of unsaturated compounds.   Thus the hydrogenation of oils into hardened fats; the hydrogenation of benzene to cyclohexane and of phenol to cyclohexanol (hexalin).

To Georges Patart in France is accredited some

of the earliest work (1921) on the hydrogenation of carbon monoxide. Methyl alcohol is now synthesized by passing a mixture of these gases under pressure over a heated zinc oxide-chromic oxide-copper catalyst. This process was first commercialized in 1923 in Germany. Today we have a superabundance of methyl alcohol. Its further treatment with carbon monoxide leads to acetic acid. Though acetic acid today takes its rise chiefly in acetylene hydration processes, tomorrow it will come either from this carbonylation of methyl alcohol or from the oxidation of ethyl alcohol.

This application of carbon monoxide to methyl alcohol synthesis saved the day for the calcium carbide furnaces from which one molecule of carbon monoxide is produced per every molecule of calcium carbide. A portion of this carbon monoxide is now made to react with water to yield carbon dioxide and hydrogen; the former is sold as dry ice and the latter brought into reaction with the remaining portion of carbon monoxide in methyl alcohol synthesis.

Just as with carbon monoxide so with coal and oil and other such material with hydrogen under pressure. Here Friederich Bergius in Germany has succeeded in driving such hydrogenation to yield gasoline hydrocarbons. Franz Fischer in

Germany has obtained oils and hydrocarbons direct from carbon monoxide and hydrogen.

POLYMERIC COMPOUNDS

The first plastic compound to enter commercial production was celluloid, the homogeneous solution of camphor and nitrocellulose discovered by J. W. and I. S. Hyatt in this country in 1869. It was placed in manufacture in 1874. The condensation of phenol and formaldehyde leads to highly complex polymeric compounds. By control of this condensation Leo Baekeland in 1909 in this country discovered an admirable substitute for amber and other natural plastics. He called the product Bakelite. Phthalic anhydride and glycerol yield glyptal and hosts of other combinations are known. The principal difficulty it seems is the cost of manufacture of moulding compound. Formaldehyde certainly will drop in price as it is one step in the methyl alcohol synthesis. Possibly, as it becomes known that orthoxenol (orthophenyl phenol) and its derivatives offer the highest germicidal properties coupled with nontoxicity to man, then a tremendous demand for this by-product in the hydrolysis of chlorobenzene by the Hale-Britton process may force down the cost on the main product phenol. At least when phenol and formaldehyde each sell for one-half their present day prices, we may expect to see a real advance in synthetic resins. Hard wood will be completely substituted.

METALS

In the realm of metals and their alloys there is a growing interest in material resistant to weather. The alloys of iron with nickel and chromium bring out these distinctive features. Indeed old-fashioned steel is on its death bed. Tungsten, chromium, manganese, and molybdenum are gaining rapidly in the metal world.

In 1886 Charles Hall in this country discovered that metallic aluminum could be obtained by the electrolysis of bauxite in a molten cryolite (sodium aluminum fluoride) bath. In 1888 a small plant was erected and placed in operation. The application of aluminum to numerous and varied purposes has surpassed all expectations. Its principal alloy is known as Duralumin (containing about 4 per cent copper, 0.5 per cent manganese, and 0.5 per cent of magnesium and its silicide). An alloy of aluminum covered with pure aluminum is called "Alclad." Beryllium has been alloyed with aluminum and especially with copper to serve good purposes; beryllium bronzes are highly resistant to fatigue. Though the cost of producing beryllium is about $10.00 per pound, its valued properties more than offset this cost factor.

Beginning with World War days the element magnesium received marked attention. This metal is one-third lighter than aluminum and even one-thirtieth lighter than beryllium. It is the lightest of all moisture-proof metals. In Germany its alloy with aluminum and zinc is known as Elektron-metal. In this country its alloy Dow-metal, embracing, a wide range of compositions, is typically represented as containing about 6 per cent aluminum and about 0.5 per cent manganese. It is easily workable under all conditions and naturally this lightest air-stable metallic alloy that man can ever have is destined to meet with rapidly extending uses, especially in airplane and automobile industries.

THE CHEMICAL TREND

It is interesting to note the turn in synthetic rubber that may follow the work of Wallace Carothers in this country on chloroprene. This compound is the counterpart of isoprene in which the methyl group of the latter stands replaced by chlorine. Chloroprene is readily polymerized to a synthetic rubber known as Duprene. The presence of the chlorine atom actually rendering the finished product more resistant to the deteriorating effects of oxygen of the air. In ordinary rubber the application of a wide range of anti-oxidants insures against such disintegration.

In 1892 the discoveries of Cross and Bevan in England on cellulose and its conversion into a sodium cellulose, with final transformation by action of carbon bisulphide into a soluble cellulose xanthate, offered immediate possibilities of repre-cipitating the cellulose from this "viscose" state into the form of threads. Such is rayon or re-generated cellulose (in sheet form and rendered pliable by admixture with glycerol, it is known as cellophane). Other methods have come into use. Notably the reduction of nitrocellulose; the dis-solving of cellulose in copper ammonium solution and reprecipitation; and particularly the produc-tion of cellulose esters (as cellulose acetate or celanese) and their direct employment in the arts. Derivatives of these products by higher acids are now in the making. They will revolutionize the rayon industry.

The maceration of woody materials into pulp of high cellulosic content has long been in operation and increasing amounts are in demand. The hydrolysis, however, of cellulose and starch by dilute acids into dextrine and finally glucose is the outstanding development in commercial reversion of one of nature's great steps. The Bergius process for glucose direct from sawdust calls for hydrochloric acid, and the method devised for recovery of this hydrochloric acid makes for an economical operation. There would seem to be ample reason for the conversion of these highly abundant and cheaper natural products into simpler units, when further adaptabilities to new and more complex compounds are desirable.

In a progressive world there is abundant evidence of a drift to the use of more and more complex types of compounds, especially where requirements call for some desirable specificity of properties. Phenol and its methyl derivatives (the cresols) of the past generation are now giving way to ortho-xenol (orthophenyl phenol) of the present; nontoxicity to man and absence of odor markedly enhance its medicinal value to say nothing of germicidal strength many, many times that of the old-fashioned phenol. In the field of synthetic resins it is the para-xenol (paraphenyl phenol) and similarly substituted higher derivatives that command choice over phenol; but here the qualification sought in finished plastic is durability and high melting point.

The entire field of dyes and aromatic derivatives, especially those compounds exhibiting specific resistance to destructive agents (fastness), and specific smoothness in pharmacological action, (tolerance), respectively, is entering upon more complicated ring structures; particularly where such structure contributes less failingly to the magnification of whatever property desired. Thus the perylene ring complex (of Zinke) and just this year the coronene ring (of Scholl), a hexabenzobenzene or a benzene nucleus built into six completely encircling benzene nuclei, offers most entrancing leads.

The biological hydrogenation of carbon dioxide has been demonstrated as far back as 1910 by Soehngen. Carbon dioxide and hydrogen brought in contact with putrifying bacteria yield methane. Recently Franz Fischer isolated from sewage certain bacteria that actually were able to reduce carbon monoxide with hydrogen into methane. There was found to arise to some extent an equilibrium between carbon monoxide and water as against carbon dioxide and hydrogen. It is possible that carbon dioxide and hydrogen are first converted into formic acid and then into acetic acid as intermediate products; at all events methane was the end product. It is known that fish in some way are able to hydrolyze chlorobenzene into phenol. Who knows but that some day the work of a corps of cold blooded animals will replace a high temperature, high pressure installation as of today.

Life, after all, is just a balance between the microorganism in its work on building up, tearing down, and building up compounds and the macroorganism (man) and his building up, tearing down, and building up compounds. Industry, however, is continually bringing into play greater and more powerful forces. To such ends a stupendous outlay of energy has proved necessary. As we progress still further we shall undoubtedly make use of these simpler steps outlined by nature and in which all is so cheaply and unerringly accomplished and with smallest expenditure of energy.

Industry in the broader sense took its rise midst the developments here enumerated. That intense urge to synthesize indigo pointed the way and the demands created in its actual manufacture broadened the road till industry was able to produce substantial quantities of chlorine, caustic soda, sulphuric acid, and resistant metals, and by no means least a generous supply of electric energy. Before 1890 an electric generator above the toy stage was unobtainable.

The stupidity of her political leaders has ever militated against a nation's advance. Those who could not envisage the vast array of organic syntheses that lurked within the coal-tar wastes of fifty years ago suffered Germany to attain intellectual and industrial supremacy. Today there are those who cannot see the glorious possibilities and transcendent syntheses that are to arise in the carbohydrate domain. Insofar as they are able to repress the translation of such researches into practice, to exactly that degree will their countries retrogress. No matter what the gold and armament at their service their peoples will beg alms at the hands of the carbohydrate chemical nations.

CHAPTER V

THE CHEMICAL REVOLUTION

There is no animosity between the chemist and the toiler of the land; they are each striving to provide for man's needs at lowest costs. As biology develops, the chemist in turn will apply his art to extend and diversify the output of the land. But, from time to time the advance in chemical manufacture is destined to work havoc upon century old customs and habits.

Some 400,000 acres, extending from France into Asia Minor were once under cultivation of madder. By 1870 the annual world crop of this root had mounted to 70,000 tons, valued at that time 'at $15,000,000.00 and containing about 1,500,000 pounds of pure alizarin. In 1912 the consumption of synthetic alizarin amounted to 4,000,000 pounds. Today little or no madder is grown. Synthetic alizarin was victorious.

In the same manner, natural indigo was practically driven from the world market by the synthetic product. This constituted the greatest chemical gamble in the world's history down to the close of the nineteenth century. Over $5,000,000.00 was expended by the German companies toward their goal. No one could have foreseen the tremendous obstacles that were destined to beset the enterprise.

The average annual world production of indigo in 1880 amounted to some 8,000,000 pounds (65 per cent indigotine). In 1896 approximately 1,600,000 acres under indigo cultivation yielded a crop of 17,000,000 pounds of indigo (65 per cent indigotine) valued at $20,000,000.00. In 1912, after fifteen years of severe competition, this acreage had dropped to 200,000 and the value of the crop to about $2,000,000.00. In 1913 Germany exported 13,400,000 pounds (100 per cent) synthetic indigo valued at $10,000,000.00 with the selling price reduced to about one-half of what the natural indigo commanded in 1896. By 1914, synthetic indigo in the form of a 20 per cent paste was being delivered in New York at 15 cents per pound. Today the world production of indigo (20 per cent) is about 75,000,000 pounds annually. The victory was complete. Synthetic indigo of American manufacture appeared in our markets in January, 1917. From its initial selling price of $1.25 per pound (20 per cent paste) the constant lowering in manufacturing costs permitted of its sale at scarcely 13 cents per pound by 1927.

As with dyes, so also must we take cognizance of the time factor governing other striking discoveries and their commercial adaptations. In plastics the commercial production of bakelite was under way as early as 1910. By 1913 in this country over a thousand employees were at work in the manufacture of bakelite buttons alone. By 1922 over 6,000,000 pounds of synthetic resin (bakelite) was being produced in the United States; by 1924 this quantity had been doubled.

In the field of textiles the substitution of natural silk by several varieties of synthetic silk-like fibre constitutes a most striking period in world history. In 1889 Count Hilaire de Chardonnet at Besançon, France, built the first plant for conversion cf wood pulp into artificial silk through nitration followed by denitration, yet by 1900 only a few thousand pounds per year measured the total output. The first American plant for artificial silk was constructed in 1910 at Marcus Hook, New Jersey; it was the viscose silk type as introduced in England by Cross and Bevan.

As late as 1912, America imported 1,500,000 pounds of artificial silk. By 1920 the American plants were producing 8,000,000 pounds of rayon, and by 1926, 60,000,000 pounds, of the then total world production of 2,000,000,000 pounds. In 1921 we consumed in this country about 18,000,000 pounds of artificial fibre and in 1931 as much as 150,000,000 pounds. This large quantity, however, constituted but 5 per cent of the total textile fibres consumed here in 1931. The critical factor is that between 1921 and 1931 there is registered no overall increase in consumption of other than artificial fibres. As this competition between natural textile fibres (cotton, silk, and wool) and artificial fibres increases, we shall see a retrogression of land from such cultivation as cotton.

In the field of fertilizers and explosives we come upon one of the greatest discoveries as yet made by modern man in his mastery over nature; side by side with the invention of the steam engine ranks this great discovery. This is the direct synthesis of ammonia from hydrogen and atmospheric nitrogen.

To Fritz Haber and his co-workers in Germany—between 1903 and 1913—falls the honor of this great achievement. In.this undertaking, tremendous financial and scientific assistance was thrown into the effort, the like of which the world had never before known. Success was replete. The plant for the Haber-Bosch process was built at Oppau, near Ludwigshafen, and began actual production of ammonia in a commercial way in September 1913. The capacity of this small plant at first was 7,000 tons fixed nitrogen per year. During the world war it reached 60,000 tons. This same company started production of ammonia in April 1917 at another plant set up at Leuna, Germany; this latter plant within one year reached a capacity output of 130,000 tons annually. In 1928, the production in Germany exceeded 400,000 tons fixed nitrogen per year, or more than the equivalent of nitrogen in total annual export of sodium nitrate from Chile. Today Germany's productive capacity of fixed nitrogen is over 1,000,000 tons and the total of other countries equally as much.

Upwards of forty years this steady encroachment upon nature, as direct source of supplies to man's needs, was steadily gaining momentum. Agriculture and mining suffered particularly at the hands of the chemist. Certain disaster threatened, yet no one knew how to avert the cataclysm. The commercial production of ammonia from its elements was the last straw; the world was thrown into turmoil.

Now the security of any nation, in a modern sense, rests primarily upon her natural resources, coupled with chemical, physical and biological researches. On such criterion Germany, at the close of 1913, had attained the utmost security; in truth she had become master of the world. This one nation had mastered a technique capable of affording unlimited supply of explosives. In common parlance this means at minimum a two year's jump on any other nation, no matter if made up of the most learned men on earth; costly experience on the part of every modern manufacturer has fully verified this time-advantage. Thus with Germany in possession of greater latent physical power than any other nation it is not difficult to understand the pre-war tenseness and strained relations between European Nations.

The world war arose through commercial rivalry between these European nations; a rivalry made all the more intense by reason of Germany's growing prowess in chemical and physical science.

At the opening of hostilities in 1914, the German military machine functioned well. It failed, however, at points where resistance built up. At such stage, on April 22, 1915, chlorine gas, at the suggestion of her chemists, was brought into the fray. Thus was inaugurated modern or chemical warfare.

Now the odd thing about the world war is that Germany, though skilled in chemical pursuits, did not realize her own Herculean power when armed with the mightiest weapon yet given to man.

The possibilities of chemical warfare surpass all limits to human imagination. But in its early days a complete and close coordination between aery, army and navy through chemical and physical direction was, after all, too much to expect of any nation.

In future conflicts the supreme directorates will be in the hands of chemists, physicists, biologists and engineers. Looking to this service, the chemists of today are actively engrossed. Ridiculous in the extreme are the pronouncements of this or that seat of antiquity concerning the requirements of future combatants to use only medieval weapons. To wide awake nations medieval weapons with shot and shell are taboo.

The delays encountered by Germany in perfecting her chemical attacks spelled her own doom. In failing to grasp and utilize an acknowledged two-year time-advantage, she gave to the Allies their opportunity to meet the attack and surpass it. Germany virtually forced her opponents to become chemically conscious and chemically fit and overpoweringly so.

Future generations will describe this cataclysmic period of history as the counterpart of that great upheaval in the march of European civilization caused by the invention of the steam engine. Man power was there supplanted by the machine, culminating in the great mechanical revolution of the last quarter of the eighteenth century. This first great revolution in man's history extended over 35 to 40 years, simply by reason of delayed scientific applications and curtailed extensibility of financial credits. In many parts of the world it was little felt. In this country, the trek westward operated more to hasten demand for machinery in the Eastern States and to speed up construction of steam operated railways for connecting frontiers with home cities.

We are now in the second great world revolution. The economists of the future will attribute the cause of this second cataclysm to the increasing replacement on large scale of much of nature's output by direct chemical adaptations springing from the genius and industry of man. On the other hand, adaptations of agricultural resources to fit into the changing chemical world were totally neglected; hence the upheaval. The stage was admirably set for this chemical revolution even in 1913, with the replacement of naturally occurring nitrates by the synthetic product. It needed only a spark to set off the world war that came in 1914. The urge to produce gained increasing momentum, with only a slight setback during a few years following the war, till in 1929 financial credits were broken. As credit had been extended both here and in all parts of the world, everything that could be marketed was rushed to sale at highest prices, no matter what the intrinsic worth. The result was destined to be a panic.

Following this great panic came deflation, and the return to normalcy, or that state characterized by a return of prices on basic products to levels commensurate with true chemical values. In opposition to this necessary trend, attempts of late have been made to bolster up commodity prices by artificial means: Such for example as the stabilization schemes for rubber, coffee, sugar and wheat. All such attempts of interference with the laws of supply and demand have, and always will, come to the same dismal end—failure.

At the outbreak of the war, almost all countries, outside of Germany, were woefully deficient in chemical experience. This was by far their greatest weakness. Had Germany left her land troops at home and concentrated upon chemo-aerial attack, the victory would have been hers even within ten days. This is on the assumption, of course, that she could have commanded a great number of airplanes and a sufficiency of chemicals.

The status of chemical industry in America in 1914 was infantile in the extreme. There was only a smattering of an organic chemical industry but the inorganic had made some real progress in production of halogens, soda, sulphuric acid, and aluminum. The World War practically set up an embargo in this country on chemicals. Chemical activities thus were encouraged and, to extend this activity, an organic chemical embargo was continued after the war up to the time of passage of the benign Fordney-McCumber Tariff Act of 1922. Thus was made possible the rise and development in America of this fundamental industry of industries. Truly the Fordney-McCumber Tariff Act will be viewed by future historians as one of the greatest and most timely acts of a United States Congress in making for American safety and security for all time.

The industrial advance attained in this country during the War and in the years subsequent thereto attracted to our shores many noted economists of Europe. In their reports emphasis is laid primarily upon mass production, unlimited home markets, and a protective tariff as the three basic factors contributing to this progress.

Particularly is it to be noted that the period just following the World War chronicles our chemical awakening; it marks too our coming into realization that all industry is basically chemical. Even the smallest of nations has been just as adept at learning this great lesson of the war. Those in control of the basic chemical industry of

a nation control that nation.   Thus foreign countries would gladly pay our government an annual
stipend of two to three billion dollars if we would
agree to remove import duties on basic chemical
products alone.   Furthermore they would be
quick to remove every vestige of their tariffs
against us and pray on bended knee that we increase our other tariffs sky high.

Smaller nations, however, will need be grouped
together to insure some degree of efficiency in
manufacture and sufficiency in consumption.
High tariff barriers have sprung up everywhere as
the aftermath of this chemical revolution.   It is the
nationalistic urge to become self-supporting; and
to this end chemical adaptations in particular are
now found highly contributory.   The retaliatory-
tariff excuse set up by astute foreign politicians is
only a sop to the gullible,—the chemically un-
conscious.   Post-war tariffs must be looked upon
as national defense measures; without them the
nations would have overrun each other.

As the spirit of international good will returns
we may confidently expect these tariffs to come
again within the foreign-under-domestic cost
range.   Wherever domestic selling prices ascend
above the tariff plus world prices, provisions
should be made for importations at reduced rates
till equilibrium is restored.

Political historians of the old school would have us believe that present-day conditions are the direct result of the World War, high tariff schedules, war reparations and "irrational" bankers' loans abroad. As a matter of incontrovertible fact the conditions throughout the world today are the direct result of the stubbornness and unwillingness of man to adjust himself to scientific advance, thereby inviting wars, disaffections, unemployment and all manner of punishment nature may yet have in store for us.

The status of today has been long in the making—starting as far back as with indigo manufacture in 1897. We would have reached a climax possibly between 1915 and 1920 even had there been no sign of war. The war did come as the first crash in a disordered world. Our own over-extended credit (fictitious prosperity) and loans abroad, served to extend the inflation to the far corners of the earth. The present is just the resultant deflation from such orgies in which we are chiefly to blame; but we share with all suffering humanity in having violated every principle of chemical dictum.

External forces had little or nothing to do in the matter of keeping our own house in order. We might just as well presume that the inhabitants of Mars exert an influence upon us. We have been remiss in so much that it is difficult now to reorganize society upon a scientific basis. Nevertheless it behooves each and every citizen at earliest opportunity to engage upon truly constructive work,—this is the greatest essential to prosperity. In the chapters following is presented an outline of these immediate needs and the countless efforts called for on the part of all toward raising the standards within the four basic activities of man. These demands far outstrip the hopes of accomplishment within the life span of a generation. The course, however, is perfectly clear and we should have the zeal and courage to follow our scientific leaders.

We may consider the present deflation, following the debacle of 1929, as at lowest ebb. In fact 1932 may be considered as the closing year of the great chemical revolution beginning back in 1914. Some commodity prices have sunk too low but readjustments will soon be under way. The year 1933 will register the first step in the normal road; chemical values henceforth must serve as criteria for practically all products of industry. Upon such valorization we shall go forward to newer and better attainments than ever known. Truly a chemical revolution was nature's own method of instilling these principles into the make-up of recalcitrant man.

CHAPTER VI

MINING IN A CHEMICAL WORLD

THE FIRST of man's basic activities is mining. Paleolithic man mined well-surfaced stones to serve him in quest of game; flint quarries were his great asset. Neolithic man, known as the first agriculturist, was also the first manufacturer as evidenced in the construction of his huts. With the advent of bronze and smelting processes, requiring a supply of bronze ores brought in over trade routes, we note material advance in manufacture as well as in transportation. Mining, agriculture, and manufacture are served by transportation. The clerical, legal, financial, and even hygienic administration appertaining to any or all of these basic activities can be comprehended, of course, by the specific activity itself; thus within these four fundamental categories become centralized the whole of man's life work.

From the discovery of fire down to the Christian Era wood has served as chief of fuels. The burning of coal is mentioned by the Greek writer Theophrastus in 371 B.C. Possibly the first authentic record of its use as camp fuel falls to the Romans during their occupation of Britain. Coal is the chief residual product of decomposition of cellulosic or plant life, mainly of the carboniferous period. Petroleum on the other hand is the residual product of decomposition of marine plant and animal life, brought about through the geophysical influences of intermittent pressure and heat.

Metallic oxides, carbonates, sulphides, sulphates, phosphates, silicates, and nitrates make up the large proportion of our useful minerals. The reduction of zinc oxide by methane to give metallic zinc at one-fifth the cost by old-time procedure involving coke, is now an accomplished fact. The reduction of iron oxides by natural gas piped to the vicinity of the mines will inaugurate a truly forward step in production of iron. It will be a simple task to lower costs under the obsolete process now in vogue where iron ore, of about 50 per cent iron content, is hauled many miles to meet with the reducing agent coke, an equal quantity of which as coal was burned to produce this form of carbon.

An outstanding example of delayed advance in metallurgy is in the preparation of aluminum. This element constitutes over 7 per cent of the entire earth crust. The most abundant of all metals, and yet it is more expensive than metallic sodium or potassium. The chemist must solve this problem and solve it soon. It should be possible to prepare aluminum direct from its double silicates with the alkali metals, the feldspars, and at a cost permitting of its sale at half the present market price, when we realize that the by-products, or potassium salts, are in wide demand.

Possibly the two greatest minerals in service of man are salt and water. Salt is the source of caustic soda and soda ash and chlorine. Water is the key to agricultural success. It is in the distribution of gas, coal, oil, salt, and water that mining as an industry is now primarily concerned. These natural resources do not belong exclusively to any individual or state. They are the property on last analysis of the Federal Government. It is the duty of those engaged in mining and in transportation to work together to the public good. No transfer from present ownership of mines need be considered when once a system for national distribution is devised.

The storage and distribution of water will ever constitute the greatest of mining enterprises. Strange that so little progress in this direction is now in evidence; ancient Babylonians realized more than we the need of water. Possibly our

dereliction in this direction lay in the tremendous
present-day cost of unsatisfactory pipe lines,—
obsolete simply because they should be made of
laminated plastic materials and at a cost for 2-inch
pipe of not over five cents per pound foot. When
this is accomplished, then water will be on tap
everywhere at all times. Our rivers shall right-
fully flow backwards and we no longer shall sit as
dotards watching the rivers flow down to the
seas—there to be impurified and rendered un-
serviceable to man, till the Heavens reevaporate
a portion and in due time send it hither and thither
and sometimes where it is needed. If Heaven
helps those who help themselves, there would
appear to be little reward for helpless man.
Over 300 pounds of water must be evaporated from
a growing plant in order to synthesize one single
pound of product. If you would grow farm produce, there is nothing so important as a good line
on a water supply.

The control of vast resources of naturally occurring minerals falls properly under the Federal
Government. Laws that will curb an over production of any one mineral may serve as tem-
porary aid but in the end there must be something
definite established on a contractual basis between
the mine operators and the consumers. There is
little hope for our mineral industries till this sys-

tem is adopted. Without this system coal can never be anything else than a waste. Oil can be no better. It were far better for humanity if all the coal and oil could be consumed by fire ere the morrow's dawn and the dread of this millstone round our necks forever dissipated. Chemists know now in all detail how we shall proceed to supply the world with all of the natural gas, petroleum, and carbon the dear old world will ever be able to use; and strange as it seems, our synthetic fuels will be available at cost, little removed from their average priced counterparts of today. Indeed it is this phantom or spectre of synthetic fuels at low cost that will forever keep coal and petroleum and gas at price levels commensurate with their chemical values.

When the synthetic fuels attain a higher heat value than natural fuels, per unit of weight, then competition will be rife.

Here is an instance that may illustrate the stupidity of man when he attempts to belittle the scientists' accomplishments as of no immediate purport. The idea of coal and oil and gas being produced more cheaply than he can dig them out of the ground irritates his entire make-up. But such an event is by no means impossible; in fact it is already an accomplished fact in experimental degree. Advice conscientiously given to all is simply this: Use all the coal and the oil and the gas as rapidly as you can at lowest prices—something far better is in the offing. However, it is confidently expected that the conversion of coal *in situ* direct into gaseous products will offer the immediate step for advance.

It is interesting to contemplate what is often called the "Divine Plan." Man arose through milleniums of time out of the ninety-two elements associated in our earthly sphere. Coexistent with man are plants and animals that contribute to his aid and subsistence. Yet aeons before his own genesis, plants and animals thrived on earth and left their decomposed selves to serve as material for the support and convenience of man that was to come. Upon the generally accepted figures of our geologists there is coal, oil, and gas within the bowels of the earth sufficient to supply all the wants of man for yet a thousand years and this even on the basis of the earth's population increasing by 50 per cent every century.

There was little real intellectual advance of man before the physico-genesis period,—the beginning of the 19th century. Real life, in other words, is just begun and in this real life the burning of fuels is proceeding at a prodigious rate. Be this as it may, the calculations of a provident Heaven have made allowance for the passage of a thousand more years before modern man will be forced to other means of securing for himself heat, light, and electricity abundant to all needs. How marvelous these calculations appear when only now it has become known that we can advance without recourse to mineral fuels. Within one hundred years, coal, gas, and oil will serve merely as additional source of power at isolated locales. At best overcalculation of eight or nine hundred years, out of the more than 1,000,000 years measuring man's life development, gives an error of less than one-tenth of one per cent on that side of the ledger that makes for the preservation of human life!

CHAPTER VII

AGRICULTURE AT THE CHEMO-GENETIC STAGE

In the adoption of the "closed field" system of agriculture, roughly dating in Europe around 1760 A.D., we find a rising incentive to improvement in soil and crops. Through countless ages the land has supported us directly with food, raiment, and shelter,—the three-fold scope of agriculture. In America the embattled farmer of revolutionary days is symbolic of the master-builder of the Nation; he constitutes the backbone of our independence.

The great mechanical revolution, 1780 to 1825, bore down much more severely upon the urban population than upon the rural by reason of a centralization within the cities of hand operating machines. In the great chemical revolution of 1914 to 1932, the blow has fallen alike upon the residents of both city and farm. In recent years the drift to the cities has brought the population of the latter to over 56 per cent of the whole; whereas, by January 1, 1930, scarcely 44 per cent represented the rural population (inclusive of villages up to 2500 persons.) Unemployment, therefore, within the cities makes more acute the discontent from lowered demand for farm products. Then too, the steady scientific advance contributing to higher efficiency in agriculture records itself in an expanding oversupply of farm staples. In no sense is this condition the fault of the farmers; they are following their natural bent. The fault lies at the doors of financiers and the agricultural departments of State and Nation.

Needless to remark that by reason of the present oversupply in agricultural staples, we are witnessing today about the lowest market prices these products have known for many years. If basic commodities become stabilized at present prices, we shall have indeed a wonderful foundation upon which to build for the future.

The present plight of the farmer has been prophesied for years. Chemists cried aloud, as it were, from the housetops to beware,—but echo was the only answer to their wailing cry. For the nonce the abnormal conditions of the world war served to buoy up the farmers' hopes; but in the end came the crash even with greater force.

It is not that the old-time three-fold scope of agriculture has lost significance. Each factor commands attention but there has occurred a shift in their relative weighting for society. Further-more, a fourth factor has come to the fore and by the laws of science is destined to outstrip the others; this is the supply of raw material to chem-ical industry. Possibly we should now look upon agriculture as of four-fold scope. In another sense however, we are witnessing the broadening of old-time farming into a new agricultural industry, now to be interpreted as the domain of chemogenetics; that is, the growing of chemicals through bio-logical means and to chemical ends.

As regards *shelter*, we no longer look upon lumber as the ideal building material. It is com-bustible and highly deteriorative. Bricks, tile, cement, and steel offer greater advantages. Wall board and plastics are fast replacing interior dressing and finishing. The utilization of wood flour together with condensing nuclei of organic chemical molecules—i.e., substances capable of polymerizing into compounds of a structure like to cellulose itself—undoubtedly will serve as future building material. When these plastic mixtures are employed in association with rustless steels and light alloys, home will be "Paradise enow." Sup-plies from the farm for direct shelter will tem-porarily diminish but as time passes will again return through indirect agencies.

In the matter of *raiment*, the introduction of

artificial silk has attained vast proportions. As already noted, cotton is experiencing no increase in use. α-Cellulose, of 95 to 96 per cent purity now obtainable from wood, is marketable at about 4 cents per pound. Thus is driven down the price of short staple cotton, of 96 to 97 per cent α-cellulose content, to commensurate values. A definite demand for cotton will continue of course but, in the main, its selling price must be established on its chemical value or α-cellulose content. When woody material is more cheaply grown, so likewise will cotton drop in price, but when cotton is more desirable, as in manufacture of cellulose acetate silk (celanese), then a premium will arise.

The substitution of wool by a curly rayon, soft to the touch, is already in use, but a better product is awaited. The correct substitute should be a basic derivative of some super-nuclear compound of textile properties,—both soft and warm to the touch. It is evident, therefore, that the raiment factor in old-time agriculture is losing caste in favor of stronger and lighter raw material. Nevertheless, the farm still holds the future of raiment and, if properly directed, will supply these raw materials in steady and gainful output.

The *food* factor, on the other hand, has maintained its pristine status. In fact, it is advancing steadily through diversification yet not in poundage. Illustrative of wheat flour consumption in America our per capita consumption for 1889 was 224 pounds; whereas for 1929, it was only 175 pounds. Previous to 1915, livestock consumed the greater portion of our food staples. The war depleted our horse and mule population by 25 per cent or more and the tractor has operated to repress any marked recovery. Furthermore, within the last ten years, there has occurred an appreciable drop in per capita consumption of meats, possibly 10 per cent; yet in general the total annual per capita poundage consumption of food products has remained almost constant.

Of the more than 350 million acres under crop cultivation in America, it can easily be demonstrated that 200 million acres alone will suffice, when properly farmed, for the total food and raiment requirements of all living things in this country. Now the enormous excess in acreage, over and above that necessary to assure an average yield, is largely inclusive of what is called submarginal lands or land incapable, without high expense, of average crop yields. The Federal Government has always endeavored to correct disparities in agriculture in the realization that a profitable agricultural industry betokens a prosperous state. This is a pronunciamento beyond cavil.

In 1929 the United States Congress created the Federal Farm Board as an agency to serve the farmer in the marketing of farm products. Tremendous were the possibilities inherent in this type of organization backed by 500 million dollars of Government funds. Under scientific management this Board might have turned the lot of agriculture from one of misery to one of glory and this within the short span of five years. But politics, of mean repute, evidently gained the upper hand. Here was a magnificent chemical, physical, and biological problem and all chemists, physicists, and biologists completely eliminated from decisions affecting its policies!

It is needless to recall the many panaceas proposed for the farmer's ills or to recount the many acts of Congress, carrying appropriations of billions of dollars, designed to ameliorate his sufferings. All attempts thus far in governmental action have come to the same sad end—failure; and all future attempts, eliminative of chemical and biological direction, are destined to the same untimely end. There can be only one practical solution: A scientific management with financial assurance of real contracts. Those who would promote this greatest industry that Heaven can ever give to mortal man must rid themselves of all political and fanatical taint; they must envisage here a chemical industry operating biologically for the betterment of society.

There is a fetish among many economists,—and all politicians, that prosperity on the farm will follow a proper adjustment of acreage under cultivation to average crop demands; a perfectly sound and logical argument up to, but not following, the chemical revolution. In other words, the farmer is to increase his risks to the maximum per acre, and this in spite of increasing ravages year by year of insect pests and the uncontrollable conditions of weather. It is unreasonable in the extreme. We should be devoutly thankful that the farmer has cultivated in excess in order that humanity be assured against calamities.

Now the correct scientific procedure is to encourage the farmer to produce all he can of everything he can in every way he can but on as small an acreage as is commensurate with his immediate and surrounding markets. We should never discourage an excess of so little as 25 per cent in output above national requirements.

The guiding principle underlying modern agriculture rests in the contracts per acre for output which the agriculturist makes with the surrounding industries capable of consuming or reconverting such output. Whatever acreage is not thus included under contracts should be planted to trees, shrubs, and other slow growing flora.

In the far south of this country, reaching inward some fifty miles from the Gulf of Mexico, nothing gives greater promise than the tung tree. This tree will come into bearing within five years to yield as much as 1500 pounds of tung oil per acre and commanding easily 4 to 5-cents per pound. North of the tung tree region, to the East, we should grow ramie, or china grass, for the strongest of all known natural fiber. An invention, however, is here required to simplify and speed up decortication of plant stalk. To the west we may still grow cotton. North of the ramie and cotton belt, to the East, we should grow long leaf and loblolly pine, which when not exceeding ten years' growth is to serve admirably for paper pulp. The City of Savannah is becoming chemically conscious in this particular endeavor; success will reward her. To the West in this belt pecans and other nut trees are highly suitable. Throughout the South many annual plants as the sweet potato and peanut are yet to be developed.

In the middle tier of states, we should cultivate hybrid poplar for a short pulp fiber and also a great variety of fruit trees and vegetables. Westward the soy bean and corn as annual crops for oil and starch and most important of all, the Jerusalem artichoke (Helianthus tuberosus) for levulose. The tubers of this plant contain the starch-like substance known as inulin and this, upon hydrolysis, yields levulose (fructose), just as ordinary starch yields glucose. From ten to twenty tons of these tubers (yielding 15 per cent levulose) may be grown per acre with little cultivation.

This levulose sugar, (which we may term "luvose" in contradistinction to glucose or dextrose) is associated, as we have seen, with glucose in an equimolecular combination through loss of 1 molecule of water to give 1 molecule of sucrose (or what is commonly called cane or beet sugar). Upon hydrolysis, a molecule of sucrose is in turn resolved into 1 molecule of luvose and 1 molecule of glucose. Such hydrolytic reaction begins immediately that sucrose is taken into the human system but is completed only after several hours.

The annual consumption of sugar in this country is about 110 pounds per capita. Then too over 1 per cent of our population is diabetic and diabetes is known to result through an intolerance to sucrose sugar. Levulose is an excellent glycogen (animal fat) producer and yet does not cause a rise in hyperglycemia (blood sugar). This characteristic of levulose, distinguishing it above other sugars, is no doubt due to its slow rate of absorption and high rate of conversion into glycogen; in 4 hours' time 16 per cent of the glucose absorbed in the human system is deposited in the liver as glycogen, whereas with levulose likewise absorbed, 40 per cent is so converted and deposited.

Levulose is about one and one-half times sweeter than cane or beet sugar; glucose is possibly one-half times as sweet as sucrose. As a sweetening agent, therefore, levulose will take precedence over all else; as a raw product for chemical processing, glucose should take the lead. At all events, we must needs develop these two sugars as well as sucrose for the future of our carbohydrate industries. A small operating plant for levulose production is actually now under way at Iowa State College, Ames, Iowa. The extension of this industry awaits only financial backing. Were it not for the stubbornness and selfishness on the part of the larger cane sugar interests, the farmers even now would be growing artichokes (or possibly dahlia and chicory) to supply an increasing demand for levulose (luvose). It is feared by these interests that their investments in the cane and beet sugar industries might suffer; they seem not to be concerned as to how much the farmers may be suffering now! Thus their days shall be numbered and they shall be gathered unto their forefathers, for the world is going ahead chemically and they are not a part thereof.

The central and north central region of the country will continue as our great wheat belt. It is here that the cost of production makes possible a selling price on the farm of 50 to 75 cents per bushel. When we overstep this latter price on the present valuation of the dollar, we overstep the chemical value of wheat. In similar fashion the selling price of corn on the farm cannot overstep 50 cents per bushel. We have been forced to experience the most drastic chemical revolution in order that this chemical interpretation be revealed to man. When we again encourage the return to high and exorbitant prices on our basic commodities, just so soon shall we suffer another upheaval. This verily is the modern Handwriting on the Wall.

Now the value of any commodity in a competitive world is simply that amount of standard currency which it commands in equal and open exchange. Corn might well be worth $1.00 per bushel if one desired the sum total of all the chemical components of corn associated in just those exact proportions as nature has built up in corn. But as the world advances chemically, man learns better and better how to prepare these several components and, of course, at lower and lower costs. In the case of corn, the equivalents in this cereal are readily obtainable. Corn oil or its equivalent is worth on the farm 5 cents per pound; starch, obtainable from cassava is worth on the farm 1 cent per pound; crude gluten press-cake is worth about $\frac{1}{4}$-cent per pound. These prices are the lowest now possible and include no purification steps. When then we consider one bushel of corn of 56 pounds weight and made up of 1.4 pounds corn oil, 30 pounds starch and 23 pounds corn gluten feed (hulls, etc.) we need only apply the chemical values for each component: 7 cents for the oil, 30 cents for the starch and 5.7 cents for the gluten feed to reach the figure 42.7 cents or the actual chemical value of corn on the farm.

If now we wish to consider the value of corn as a source of starch (where about 1100 pounds constitute an average yield per acre) there immediately comes into the picture the growing of cassava (tapioca) in San Domingo. There 2000 pounds of starch from cassava can be grown per acre at little expense. By the time it is purified and shipped to us, it stands at about $1\frac{1}{2}$ cents per pound. It carries no duty. Upon this basis, it is clearly indicative that our farmers cannot receive much more than 40 cents for their corn.

In the case of gluten feed, this material is of far greater value to the farmer than what is expressed as 5.7 cents on the bushel of corn. In fact this residual mass, or its equivalent, should be returned to the farmer gratis immediately upon his delivery of a contract of corn to the chemical markets. In this press-cake are found the greater part of the vitamins originally present in the kernel and particularly suited to the fattening of hogs. Hence, when the farmer undertakes to sell his corn at about 40 cents per bushel, with a drawback of 23 pounds gluten feed for every bushel, he really is selling a 33 pound bushel at 40 cents and yet getting almost all the worth of his corn as a fattening agent without having given up anything. To make the story complete, however, it is necessary for the farmer to grow some cheap wild starchy unharvestable plants for his livestock to make up for this loss in starch and oil.

The prerequisite for such transactions is a countless number of chemically operated plants with which the farmers can deal by direct contracts. As we emerge from the chemical revolution, we shall become aware of this widening out of chemical centers. Unless, however, the agriculturist in general is willing to dispose of his products strictly upon a chemical basis, there never can be any hope for agriculture!

As with corn so with all agricultural staples. We must develop their chemical utilization. More than ever to be considered are the by-products, which will make up the difference between present-day loss and a real profit. Weeds will be fondly cherished as steady income assurance. Thus the Cracca virginiana (Devil's shoestring) growing wild in southwestern states yields an extract most deadly to flies and yet harmless to man,—something like pyrethrum and derris. Anabasis aphylla (anabasine) a weed growing in Russia yields a neonicotine insecticide. These two medicinal plants are simple of cultivation; what a world of possibilities lie here dormant! What a God-send the return to this world of the seven years' famine of Egypt, were it to destroy only the blades of wheat, cotton, and corn that poked their noses above ground! Dire necessity would force us into extensive diversification of all kinds of crops. But we wouldn't suffer—no not for one moment.

The underlying principle governing the chemical interpretation of agriculture, from the standpoint of intensive crop cultivation, is embodied in the assumption that every article from the land must find storage in more or less stable form. Our warehouses must bulge with every sort of raw, half-finished and even finished products. Any large oversupply of a particular staple will, of course, operate in reduction of acreage that may be brought into contract in the following year for this staple. The full warehouses simply must

persist otherwise prices will rise out of all proportion to chemical worth and we shall be back again
on medieval footing.

When we reach a state where warehouses are
overflowing with foods, chemicals and other
finished products derived from agricultural
sources, it will be necessary to restrict somewhat
the immediate output of the farm but only as
applies to annual crops. The slow growing crops
will not be so sensitive to annual fluctuations. At
all events, a steady increase will accrue to the
farmer through regular payments, made on the
warehoused goods as fast as consumed.

During the years of over abundance in storage,
the farmers will devote their energies particularly
to drainage and water supply and soil improvement. As already discussed, this question of
irrigation is paramount to good farming. Modern
man will be looked upon as transgressors of nature
by the civilization of 2000 A.D., especially in
comparison with the neolithic civilizations of
Sumeria-Akkam and also of Egypt, when it is
known how these early peoples built and utilized
a large number of irrigation canals.

Every acre under cultivation should be provided
with a direct source of water. Our rivers are
sufficient to this enormous demand. Generally
speaking, we have not as yet begun scientific

agriculture, even though some 12,000 years have elapsed since its origin. The chemical revolution has now brought us to our senses. Agriculture appears in its true light,—that of an organic chemical and biological industry; and if we hope to enjoy life in this most wonderful laboratory of nature, we must devote ourselves to chemical and biological studies appertaining thereto. A close association between agriculturist and industrialist will make for mutual benefits of everlasting value. In truth each is dependent one upon the other for material progress.

CHAPTER VIII

MANUFACTURE ON A CHEMICAL BASIS

I~N THE~ early days of the industrial era, ushered in by the mechanical revolution, we note that England as the chief producer of steel attained industrial status before all other nations. The United States remained predominantly agricultural up to the beginning of the present century when the introduction and development of the automobile operated for our complete transformation, possibly as late as 1910.

So new indeed is this shift in this country from agricultural to industrial that in lieu of the recent return of urban unemployed back to the land it is more fitting to describe our present status as "balanced." This retreat to the land is the greatest single sign of a return to normalcy and a precursor of general employment everywhere. By January 1, 1932, our rural population (inclusive of villages of 2500) was found to have increased to 47 per cent of the whole. By 1933 this proportion should exceed 50 per cent.

It was the rapid stepping up in automobile

production, beginning about 1902 and extending through 1929, that necessitated the drain upon rural communities for labor.

The many and diverse manufacturing activities set in motion by the automobile industry defy description. It is to this diversity and particularly to the wide distribution of the supply units affecting such manufacture that we may ascribe our complete industrialization.

During the world war almost every group of men who could possibly organize and operate a manufacturing plant for the supply of some war need met with success. Following the war, many of these going plants were considerably altered. In general, however, their activities seemed to center around the automobile and its many accessories. In this industry alone there were probably 100 different automobile manufacturing companies (some only assembly plants, of course). As sheep and again as stupid sheep, many parties looked not beyond the advice of financiers and invested in what they considered a sure thing, when if chemically analyzed, there was not the slightest chance of success. Seemingly it is well nigh impossible for the average run of mankind to learn that those who are already in a going manufacturing enterprise and have good research staffs, possess at least a two years' advantage in

technique and capacity for their type of manufacture over any and all human beings who essay
to enter such enterprise.   As already noted, this
principle is corroborated day by day; and yet
man will not learn.   One need only recall the
automobile plants that have passed into oblivion
and some that are yet to go that road.

Prior to 1900, chemical and physical advances
were not such as to constitute the determinant
factors in general manufacture.   Today the ab-
solute and final determinant in all industry is the
chemico-physico-biological aspect.   This constitutes a revolution of greatest import,—the chemical
revolution as pertains to manufacture.   Henceforth the stability of any manufacturing concern
will be assessed primarily on a chemical basis.

New discoveries and adaptations in the wider
domain of manufacture will, of course, give rise to
new and independent organizations.   Likewise,
well-established organizations will use every
opportunity to improve their own output.   The
present automobile is only in its early developmental stage.   Light metals and plastics will soon
constitute its entire structure.   We have barely
touched upon correct means of attaining pronounced efficiency in combustion of its fuel.   The
exhaust vapors from the present-day motor contain carbon monoxide and other poisonous ma-

terial. To these vapors is now attributed the increase in fatalities arising from thrombosis of the brain, as affects our middle-aged population dwelling within cities. It is highly desirous that the internal combustion engine be operated on a complete combustion principle.

Though the automobile industry in the United States in 1929 attained its magnitude of almost a six billion dollar turnover and ranked second only to the petroleum industry, it must not be forgotten that both together at that time did not overtop agriculture with a fourteen billion dollar turnover. Today all of these activities are much reduced.

In the wake of the automobile came road construction and park developments. The radio, now in rapidly broadening use, will bring in home improvements and architecture. The rendering fit of air for dwellings includes a control of temperature, moisture, and suspended dust particles. We must modify these variants at will and to the establishment of a salubrious, bonairified (good air) room atmosphere for each and all. We may call the mechanism that is to serve this purpose a bonaire-motor. It is not unduly prophetic to picture the approaching *bonaire-motive industry* as more than likely to surpass the automotive industry at its heyday of expansion. As the automobile made for enjoyment of the outdoors, so likewise will the radio and television and bonaire enhance the indoors, but a modern comfortable indoors.

High pressure salesmanship, springing up in the sale of Liberty Bonds, continued unabated during and after the war in almost every direction and to such extent that by 1929 the entire populace was possessed of a plethora of indiscriminate articles that defied description. Furthermore, much of the ghastly collection as yet had not been paid for. Where vision in manufacture had become conspicuous for its absence, veracity in advertising had become astonishingly rare.

Glaring out from pictorial displays in magazines and screeching into the microphone of the radio, we are struck with much of glorified nothingness. It is the hang-over of high pressure salesmanship. The educated little heed such buffoonery. In time, a composite book displaying all makes of automobiles with their points of interest will be on call at automobile stores, garages, etc. It requires today a type of mental retrogression on the part of anyone who would purchase an automobile through advertisement without studying all other makes alike.

What thinking man would buy a proprietary preparation or toilet article recommended only by its particular manufacturer? In time a book setting forth the qualities of all these articles will be on call at drug stores. In the olden days before the chemical revolution there is no doubt but that a demoniacal drive or advertising campaign (as they called it) sufficed to satiate the gullible. Today reason has returned, the revelation of true worth to monetary value is at hand. Upon such interpretations salesmanship can truly advance.

Furthermore, when the expenses incurred by advertising and selling are reduced to a minimum; when unnecessary repackaging and relabeling are eliminated; then we shall entertain the hope that these terrific spreads between cost of production and selling price to consumers shall be brought within reasonable bounds. It is opportune that a chemico-physico-biological study of every manufacturing organization be instituted. A correct perspective of present and future activities may thus be envisaged by a group of investigators apart from those who study only the financial statements.

CHAPTER IX

TRANSPORTATION IN CHEMICAL
SERVICE

IN THE service of the three
basic activities, mining, agriculture, and manufacture, we come to the fourth basic activity of
man; namely, transportation. Since neolithic
time the horse and ox and other beasts of burden
have supplied much of the world's motive power.
The mechanical revolution,—our physico-genesis—changed all this and power acquired a new
source; the modern world was upon us.

In this country the succeeding waves of emigration westward from our eastern states established ever-retreating frontiers. The "prairie
schooner" and "pony express" gave way to the
railway bringing our many outflung settlements
closer to home folks in point of time. In England
the iron age gave way to the steel age in 1856; in
this country the year 1874, marking the construction of our first steel mill at Bessemer, Pennsyl-
vania, defines this transition as to manufacture.
Prior to this, importation of steel from Great
Britain supplied our wants. The depression of

1873 was attributable in no small way to this shift from iron to steel.

Our transcontinental railways were constructed at great cost, but the railway companies were abundantly enriched for the future through governmental land grants and mineral privileges, embracing about 150,000,000 acres. Towns sprang up along these rail arteries as mushrooms over night to give us today a veritable labyrinthian network of steel; all of this to the end that each community may have abundant access to the trading world.

Through an inheritance from frontier days and frontier methods of railroading, methods totally incongruous with a scientific world, the chief purpose of transportation, as servant to the three other basic activities of man, was rapidly becoming eclipsed. In 1906 the Federal Government came to the rescue by setting up in the Interstate Commerce Commission the power to regulate and control general railway transportation as affecting the many railway companies. Our approximately one hundred railway organizations of the country have not altogether displayed any exuberant cordiality about such control. However, all might have worked out to the good of the country as well as to the upbuilding of the railroads had it been possible for the railway companies to dismiss forever their frontier methods of business. Such methods are those that put on all charges that the public will stand and deliver at the pleasure of the railroads.

A basic principle for any well organized company is the building for future security. This principle takes precedence over the maintenance of an effective present-day plant; otherwise the business of the company is nothing but a fire-sale. The issuance of bonds by a reputable industrial corporation for whatsoever purpose presupposes the ability of this corporation to reduce these bonds in due order. Now railway corporations in general have not exhibited any haste in retiring their bonds, consequently the dividends they have paid on preferred and common stock should be looked upon as a sort of soothing balm to the body prostrate. As the fateful end approaches, less and less valuable become their certificates of stock.

In the last few months the newly organized Reconstruction Finance Corporation has undertaken to assist by loans particularly these railway companies in dire distress. Possibly this new organization may come to be looked upon here as administer of the last rites. If our railways are to be taken over by the Federal Government, they should be thoroughly scrambled with no further semblance of kindergarten block names and riddance made of all short-sighted methods of construction, operation, and financing. When such is accomplished, and not till then, the railways of this country under perhaps a dozen systems should be handed back to the bond holders. These new systems must serve the entire country, eliminating as far as possible direct entry into congested communities or cities.

Whatever may have been the cost of construction and equipment of any railway in this country in a particular year, it is a well established fact that after the lapse of ten years, this same type of construction and equipment, estimated on a like valuation of the dollar, could not much exceed 50 per cent of the original cost. This principle applies to all manufacture; so great indeed is our prowess and progress in chemical, physical and engineering science. Any new and increased valuation to land and city holdings, as well as unexpected replacements in general, naturally cannot here be taken into consideration.

In substantiation of this principle we witness a constant withdrawal of labor into new pursuits, and happily so by reason of an increasing number of workmen attaining the skilled-labor status. Advance in manufacturing technique alone has shown that, by and large, there need be employed no more than half as many men for the accomplishment of an industrial task as were required in the same task only ten years back.

The point is simply that, owing to constantly lowering costs in construction through succeeding years, it becomes possible to accomplish our various worldly pursuits at ever receding expenditures. Whatever bonds and liens may have been issued to pay for initial installations must be redeemed in accordance with this ratio as a minimum; otherwise all common stockholders in the organizations hold merely an empty bag.

Elaborate and expensive railway stations in the central portions of cities were once looked upon as advantageous to railway development and business. The exigencies of our modern world abhor such deterrents. The modern railway must be constructed for speed; i.e., elimination of all curves and grade crossings and city entrances, save through tunnels. Proper connections at stations can easily serve nearby communities and even branch trains, or diversion of special cars of through trains, may carry passengers into some particular terminus desired. Between New York and Chicago on a well appointed train, there should be neither bell nor whistle nor detectable noise. These are the heritage of tom-tom and savagery. It won't be long till the average citizen refuses to patronize trains and busses unequipped with bonaire-motor.

Passenger and freight cars must be constructed of nickel-chrome steel, magnesium-aluminum alloys, and plastics. The weight of one of our monstrosity freight cars of today is upwards of 45,000 pounds. Properly built, the weight should not exceed 15,000 pounds as maximum. Instead of hauling $1\frac{1}{4}$ pounds of train in order to carry a pound of freight as of today, we would not use more than $\frac{1}{2}$ pound of train to carry this same pound, thus making a reduction of about one-third in our cost of transportation.

The use of rubber wheels with flanges is just lately announced for individual railway coaches. The extension of this modern wheel to entire trains is a certainty in the near future. Roller bearings for movable parts have long been demonstrated as highly advantageous; several western roads already have adopted this advance. These factors taken in connection with many others will cut another one-third from our present transportation costs; thus we are brought face to face with transportation in the immediate future at approximately one-third its cost today.

Think for a moment of a fast freight train moving at slower speed than a passenger train! This is of the ancient ox-powered world. Anything over twelve hours for all through trains between Chicago and New York is the product of repressed engineering. It's a wonder though that our ordinary type of box car stands up at all. In illustration of wind resistance to forward pull and to side wabble they will be exhibited to the future generation as depicting our present day apathy to scientific advance. The correctly constructed closed freight car must be rounded somewhat and made to carry coal as well as wheat and other commodities. A roof over an open car naturally would give the car two-fold service. All medieval types of wooden construction must be banished. The new cars, as soon as slightly worn, will be returned to the manufacturing plant and be recast at only nominal cost to the transportation systems.

The dozen or less transportation systems of the immediate future will include all bus and truck service. Interchangeability or convertability of rubber wheels with flanges to flangeless wheels will make for delivery of the freight car to the door of home or place of business, simply by use of individual power units. Trucks may still serve certain purposes but they never will constitute a big individual factor. The inter-city bus will become chiefly the city-to-railway service bus. No arguments need here be presented for this summary statement. Everyone knows that traction by wheels over straight tracks requires less energy than by wheel over smooth road bed without tracks. 'Tis energy that decides.

Much of the estimated 27,000 miles of non-paying railway today can easily come into importance through these changs in transportation units.

One of the most important changes needed in transportation is that of the zoning method for fixing transportation charges on all basic natural products, such that the citizens of the country shall enjoy an equal privilege in the use of same. A manufacturing plant at the mouth of a coal mine should pay to the transportation system an excessive sum, possibly $1.00, on every ton of coal used. By such procedure the distant consumers will not be oppressed with excessive transportation charges; thus more coal will be consumed and the mine itself forced into efficient operation. In the next zone, possibly reaching 100 miles away, a charge of $1.25 may then be sufficient for transportation and at 300 miles distance $2.00 may here suffice. To further transportation in general, the coal can be hauled by the transportation systems at their convenience and thus huge piles of coal will be assembled at many points all over the country and usually at times when grain and such like are moving in the opposite direction. Consignment charges must be arranged for by the guarantors as this is a service for the good of all citizens. Coal companies should be willing to consider this type of zoning charge in order that their product will meet with greater and greater distribution.

The principle here involved is based upon general adaptability of all freight rolling stock to all heavy transportation purposes; furthermore, natural raw products actually necessary to man's needs must be in continuous supply over as wide a territory as possible and in such quantities as to maintain prices at reasonable figures.   The object here, and it should be the aim of all transportation companies, is to decentralize manufacture.   This is a *sine qua non* to the great chemogenetic developments of the immediate future.   In a word transportation will have become at last the greatest agent for chemical distribution.

CHAPTER X

HUMAN HISTORY IN CHEMICAL PERSPECTIVE

IN THE forward march of civilization, we have been made cognizant of a gradual unfolding of scientific discovery that has led to the betterment of man. In a study of mankind in general, without reference to national groups, we can now contemplate the chemical steps that have marked this progress in a chemical world.

In remotest antiquity these strides encompassed thousands of years but as we approach the modern, they are foreshortened till only today we are completing a step that embraces scarcely seventy-five years. In fact it is the curtailed span of this last step that, more than all else, indicates man has at last arrived on some higher plane. Upon this plane his entire social and political life must now be reorganized. In a broader sense, we are at the threshold of scientific enlightenment.

Early submen were in existence over a million years ago. Recent evidence points to their possible origin in some tropical country,—possibly on the lost continent of Mu in the Pacific. Their drift into Africa and Southern Asia antedated considerably their arrival in Europe. But once in Europe a study of their habitats in reference to the four epochs of the glacial age unfolds much of their developmental history.

In the chemical narrative of man, it is necessary to introduce two inorganic classifications,—the lithic (stone) and the metallic, and one organic,— the plastic.

LITHIC PERIOD

Eolithic Age—1,000,000 ± B.C. to about
200,000 B.C.

Unfashioned coliths (dawn-stones), dating from one and one half million years ago to the end of the first epoch of the Glacial Age,—almost a half million years ago, bring to us evidence of a pre-historic quasi-human being. Eolithic submen employed these selected stones for hammering and cutting.

Paleolithic Age—200,000 B.C. to 12,000 B.C.

Not until about 200,000 B.C., between the second and third glacial epochs in Europe, can we date the remains of the so-called "Heidelberg man." The climate then was warm; only rough hand axes can be assigned to this period.

In the third interglacial epoch, extending from about 100,000 B.C. to 50,000 B.C., the climate of Europe became semi-tropical. Chipped flint tools, for a diversity of use, are now met with. Possibly the so-called "Piltdown man" conforms with the sub-human inhabitants of this time.

With the coming of the fourth and last glacial epoch, about 50,000 B.C., the retreat of these prehistoric submen to caves became inevitable. Here we meet with the well-known remains of the "Neanderthal man" or "Cave man." He made use not only of chipped flint tools but likewise also of flint flakes. He had knowledge of fire, wrapped himself in skins and displayed the beginning of definite ideas regarding death as exhibited in ceremonial burials. He was hairy, thick set, stooped, and practically incapable of speech.

Toward 30,000 to 25,000 B.C., with the retreat of last glacial ice-cap, but still a cold climate in Europe, a new type of man—Homo Sapiens, advanced into Europe from the South or Southeast in pursuit of the increasing herds of game then spreading northward, over the vacated steppes. These post-glacial people were of several races, of which the Cromagnard is best known. They were truly human, possessing brain cases, hands, necks, and teeth like to ourselves. They walked erect. Known also as reindeer men, they constituted the last of the paleolithic (old stone) men.

These reindeer men possessed great skill in rough stone implements, and indeed excellent skill in bone and horn objects, such for example as their fine-eyed needles.

Their distinct characteristic is exhibited in drawings, even in polychroms, found on the walls of their caves and on objects or artifacts of antler and bone.

Neolithic Age—12,000 B.C. to 2200 B.C.

As the glacial ice retreated far to northward, about 20,000 B.C., the climate of Europe underwent a marked change. The Mediterranean Sea came into fulness and a general sinking of Europe is recorded. With increase in moisture, the entire area of Europe took on a heavy forest growth. The reindeer and no doubt most of the reindeer men wandered northeastward over the steppes of Russia.

Again a new type of man advanced from the South or Mediterranean basin. This new type is known as neolithic (new stone) man, characterized by his use of polished stone implements. Whatever late paleolithic man remained in Europe either acquired the art of the newcomers or became merged with them racially. The neolithic age is taken as the beginning of civilization. It marks the introduction of agriculture, pottery, domestication of animals, tool grinding, bow and arrow, weaving in linen and wool, and the establishment of commonweal existence as evidenced by hut-like dwellings. This age was well under way by 12,000 B.C. and extended as far as 2200 B.C.

From that early day of prehistoric man's first use of stone down to about 2200 B.C., we describe as the Lithic (stone) Period of human history. Metals had slowly come into use, as for instance the use of hammered copper tools as far back as 5000 B.C. in Sumeria and Egypt, and especially the copper saws that served for cutting the large blocks of stone for the pyramids. But the chemical discovery to open up the new period was yet to be made.

METALLIC PERIOD

Neolithic civilization suffered markedly by reason of forest growth. The many groups of peoples thereby isolated developed distinctive differences in their spoken language. Though communication in certain directions was possible by river, it was not till near the close of the neolithic age, when climate in Europe had become dry and forests had somewhat retreated, that we note again the intermingling of various races of mankind. In the meantime the chemical discovery of reduction of metallic oxides to respective

metals by charcoal had been applied to copper ores
and especially where these ores likewise contained
tin. The result, a molten alloy, could be cast
into any desired shape and bronze thus came into
commerce. It is the smelting of ores therefore
that opens up this new period in human history.

Bronze Age—2200 B.C. to 1100 B.C.

It is generally acknowledged that bronze first
came into use in the Aegean district at about 2200
B.C. In Hungary, copper and tin ores have been
found together; possibly this is the source of the
well-known leaf-shaped sword of that district in
about 1500 B.C. The use of bronze spread very
rapidly; it revolutionized the habits of man, and
made him king of earthly dominions. Naturally
it contributed nothing to the promotion of peace.
This age extended to about 1100 B.C.

Iron Age—1100 B.C. to 1856 A.D.

Some little time elapsed following the introduction of bronze before man was able to make this
same smelting process successfully applicable to
iron ores. The reason, of course, lay in his
inability to centralize a higher heating zone.
Nevertheless he did eventually secure a semi-
molten mass of iron that could be worked up in
form desired. Though iron beads and trinkets

were known in Egypt for several thousands of years beforehand, it was not till about 1300 B.C. that iron castings were made in Crete and possibly not much before 1100 B.C. in Europe in general. The use of iron spread rapidly. In certain regions of the ancient world bronze appeared almost simultaneously with iron, but in the main we must give to bronze historical priority.

Early mastery with iron implements endowed several nations with almost world power. Thus the Greeks, under Alexander the Great, owe their extension of influence to the invincibility of the Macedonian phalanx,—a massed vehicle of spear heads equally supported and controlled. The Romans spread their empire only after overcoming the Carthaginians at sea. By use of drawbridges provided with iron hooks at further ends let down upon enemy quinqueremes, the Romans rushed the Carthaginians and anihilated them. As a summary, we may conclude that through their simple iron hooks the Romans preserved Europe for the Aryan race.

Steel Age—1856 to 1932

The hardening of iron in a small way has been known for centuries. There could not be prepared, however, any appreciable quantity of steel at one time. This required the manipulation of a chemical process such as was unattainable till Bessemer in 1856 introduced his movable converter. By the Bessemer process many tons of steel of uniform composition could be made in shortest time. The commercialization of steel immediately became possible. This was the opening of the steel age. Other types of converters were soon to follow and the growth and adaptation of steel to a multiplicity of uses knew no bounds. Steel, of course, replaced iron especially where strength of material was required. Railway and automobile industries consume over three-fourths of all the steel manufactured in this country.

The development of highly hardened steels especially of non-rusting properties has come about through alloys of steel with nickel and chromium and various other elements. These new steels exhibit an equality of hardness with old-time steel of much greater cross section. They fall, therefore, into competition with the lighter metals which more and more will replace old-time steel by reason of the natural drift away from unnecessary weight when equal qualities of strength are attainable with less poundage.

Magal Age—1932 A.D. to (?)

Alloys of lighter metals particularly those of magnesium (specific gravity of 1.74) and aluminum (specific gravity of 2.70) have now been made to take on superior hardness particularly by heat treating. In fact this hardness makes them capable of replacing some of the older types of steel. Together with these light alloys, we include the rustless steels,—alloys chiefly with chromium and nickel, and which exhibit such tremendous strength in small cross section. All these taken together may be called light metal alloys and the age we are now entering may be termed the light alloy age. But representative of quantity possible of production, and thus of extensibility, magnesium and aluminum alloys offer to supply the greatest demands the world can ever present. The age, therefore, that is now upon us we call the mag(nesium) + al(uminum) or *magal* age. The steel age par excellence comprises that period between 1856 and the present or about 1930–1932. The price of steel at 2 cents per pound still holds advantages over aluminum at 20 cents, but this latter must be rated at 7 cents per equalized volume as aluminum has only one-third the specific gravity of steel. The now reduced price of magnesium at 30 cents per pound is at once equalized with aluminum at 20 cents as magnesium has only two-thirds the specific gravity of aluminum. Thus at 7 cents per unit volume of magal against 2 cents for steel and the soon to be instituted lower prices for these lighter metals, there is less and less chance for old fashioned steel to withstand the competition. Especially and more drastically will this fact be emphasized as we appreciate the value of lighter and lighter material in all walks of life;—it being understood at all times that a sufficiency of strength can be supplied by these light alloys for every requisite.

The advent of these light alloys marks the closing stage of the metallic period of human history. Though this introduction already is a fact, it is hardly proper to date their ascendency before 1932. Naturally their use will overstep steel in tonnage, but yet a few years will pass before this complete transition. Just as with the earlier ages described above, it must not be thought that any succeeding age eliminates the use of preceding art. All alloys of steel will always find specific uses.

In defining the limits of the magal age—which we are now developing, it is only reasonable to keep in mind that these same conditions that ushered light alloys to the fore will, in time, demand even greater strength of construction material with still further decrease in weight. There is no metal lighter than magnesium and stable under atmospheric conditions. Hence the next step must be in new types of alloys or, more than likely, outside the domain of pure metals, that is in the organic chemical field.

It behooves us now again to review these progressive steps in human history as they comprehend certain advances in organic chemistry. To our amazement we find no striking change in the substitution of organic chemical instruments, utensils, and building material from earliest day down to about 1910 A.D.

PLASTIC PERIOD

Paleoplastic Age—30,000 B.C. to 1910 A.D.

In nature man has found serviceable to his use any number of objects that can be cut and polished at will. Ivory, bitumen, amber, bone, and horn were known and shaped by late paleolithic man. Amber, whalebone, ebony, and the like have met with constant service. The use of these naturally occurring "plastic" products has continued from early days to the present. Organically expressed the old form of plastic material (paleoplastic) served contemporaneously with man without change from his beginning to this century. Particularly we note that about 1910 a new development occurred. This is the synthesis of plastics from liquid state and under pressure.

Neoplastic Age—1910 A.D. to 1950 ± A.D.

The early manufacture of celluloid and synthetic ivory dates back well before 1900 but about 1910 Bakelite, as a type of synthetic amber, gained extensive use in the markets of this country. Bakelite was finished from liquid or near liquid material and consequently was susceptible to molding to desired form and hardness. Its introduction, therefore, is exactly parallel to the passing from the lithic period to metallic period where smelting was introductory to, and the precursor for, such change. Synthetic resins, however, do not follow the molecular structures of their naturally occurring counterparts. In general the field of plastics comprehends resins, gums, bitumens, cellulose derivatives, and countless condensation products, all of high molecular weight and capable of being molded to form.

The Silico-Plastic Age—1950 ± to —(?)

The entire field of plastics includes a vast array of compounds and mixtures of compounds; the continued serviceability of finished form ever constituting the most valuable asset. Nature is the great plastic builder. Carbon compounds, synthesized in cells of plants, make up the greater portion, yet silicon and other elements are brought into the final structures.

In the alloying of metals we observe always the inclusion of one or more of the original free components. The strength of resulting alloy is a function of the distribution of its components in relation to each other and usually about some molecular lattice structure.

Now in the plastic world the lattice of extremely complicated molecular units is compacted densely. It is conceivable that the same strength might be attained were we to introduce a skeletal structure of yet other elements. This skeletal structure should be formed through interaction of the appropriate carbon compounds with compound of the additional element. In other words the additional element should be involved in the organic complex that makes up the lattice structure. In nature silicon is known to play a most important rôle toward imparting resistance and rigidity to the ordinary tree.

It may be assumed that the atomic structure of silicon lends itself to close alignment with carbon. The ability of silicon to hold oxygen, as evidenced in the adamantine rocks of nature, will contribute much to increase in strength of finished product.

It is further assumed that plastics incorporating a partially oxidized silicon as a component in this structure will exhibit tremendous strength and resistance to weathering and oxidation in general.

The final product will not need to exceed a specific gravity of 1.5 and thus will be capable of replacing magal and other light metallic alloys of specific gravity of 2. The tendency of most of our metals to oxidize has always been a deterrent feature. The new silico-plastic will be finished directly from molten or semi-molten state.

Undoubtedly something of the type of silico-plastic will constitute the next step forward in building material. Possibly by the date above indicated (1950) we shall have found a way to introduce metal atoms in this same molecular structure of lattice work in plastics. The only metal known so far to constitute a portion of plant growth is magnesium; which element occupies an important portion in the molecule of chlorophyll. It is possible that other metals may be found capable of such introduction. The result of a metallo-plastic compound capable of molding and exhibiting in finished form phenomenal tensile and compression strength is well worthy of our immediate researches.

In order to be strictly in keeping with past stages of man's development we shall be content to describe the future age as the silico-plastic age. Just as stone gave way to metal, thus we shall assume again the same order and the *Metallo-Plastic Age* may be awaited toward the close of this century.

Since those early days of lithic and metallic periods in human history, it is evident that the organic chemical development drifted along seemingly without purpose. When nature revealed her living self to man in 1828–1830, the pace quickened somewhat till about 1910 when organic chemistry took the lead. The old parallelism of inorganic and organic still obtains but a merge of the two is indicated for the not far distant future, when hand in hand they shall provide the most remarkable and astounding material ever conceived by mortal man.

The tall sky scrapers of today will seem as pigmies in comparison with the super-structures of tomorrow. Buildings will be moulded from plastic material poured from above. A height of 10,000 feet should offer no obstacles whatsoever. The depth in the ground need only be sufficiently extended, as at no time should the weight of buildings exceed the total weight of excavated mass.

CHAPTER XI

CHEMECONOMICS

CAPTAINS of industry have long been wont to study business methods from time-worn economic concepts. Periods of inflation were known to carry in their wake similar periods of deflation. The rising tide of prosperity in 1923–1929 was estimated as capable of thwarting any tendency toward retardation. Those in highest authority, both in government and finance, gave utterance of their credence in a new and glorious era. They never sensed the chemical clouds. They never realized the strict dependence of all things mundane upon chemical, physical, and biological principles. Theirs was a confidence that surpasseth understanding. The aftermath is known to all.

As we advance now along constructive lines, shall we be deluded again after a time or shall we take heed of the scientific status day by day? Certainly the latter offers every means to security and every urge to forward progress.

In a study of economics there are certain fundamental principles that constitute a working basis for human endeavor. When we interpret these principles primarily upon a chemical basis, their import would appear to be disconcerting in our workaday world. They are, nevertheless, worthy of diligent study. We may classify them as chemical economic concepts—possibly it were just as well to assign them to a chemical economics or what we shall call "chemeconomics."

The first principle of chemeconomics is stated as follows: *All handiwork of man disintegrates with time and, except for art or monumental structures, its valuation decreases in direct proportion to this time factor.*

Our ancient system of taxation, based upon property, is a disgrace to the scientific world. Frontier life offered little else that could be found and hence the system. Railways that were laid to serve these frontier posts and to bring ever closer the instruments to higher education were in turn subjected to penalties by way of tax. In every sense the motto of these early days seems to have been—"Bite the hand that feeds you." Upon such unsound system, taxation has continued both here and abroad.

If we should elect to continue with this unscientific system, then by decrements a tax should approach nil within 15 to 25 years, as this is the average life of any ordinary structure. Stone or monumental work naturally carries a much longer life period. At the end of the allotted time for complete amortization, the structure must be demolished. If, however, at this point there is sufficient demand for continuance in operation of structure, there should be affixed by governmental authorities a nuisance tax on same. In other words, when the property has outlived its time-period, it becomes a menace in a scientific world. A nuisance tax merely insures society against too long a menace; and as a nuisance, so also will the tax take on annual increments.

Federal and state revenues should come increasingly from nanufacturers' excise taxes and from net incomes. Under such system, we encourage continual improvements on all lands and buildings, thus creating an ever greater demand for labor. A railway company will pay state taxes on its gross receipts in that same proportion which its business within state bears to its total business.

In those cases, as with railways, where a sufficiency of maintenance work is expended upon structure to insure a definite serviceability at all times, it may be argued that the original costs, already amortized, no longer figure in the valuation. This is another way of stating that total valuation is equivalent to maintenance and replacement charges, plus bank or credit balances.

Such is not far from a true scientific intepretation. The utter absurdity of a state taxing a railway corporation on what was spent years ago is, after all, only another way of stating that dead men should be taxed. A wide awake nation sooner or later must rise in rebellion against such injustice.

The second principle of chemeconomics is stated as follows: *The best that man can do today will be antiquated on the morrow.*

When reference is made to building construction this is no other than the principle of obsolescence. Such obsolescence is usually complete within fifteen to twenty years and hence in general the amortization period likewise embraces this.

When a survey is made of man in all walks of life, it is very clear that the so-called laissez-faire policy has pervaded every civilization. It is difficult indeed to break down this old-time resistance to anything new.

It is here that we meet the rising urge to research. A goodly share of profits of a particular business must be devoted to scientific study, either directly or indirectly through well-established research institutions. The results of this research must be translated instanter into actual plant improvement or change such that an ever diversified output meets with constant demand. It is not unthinkable but that, within one decade, these studies may have brought about completely revolutionary changes within a particular plant and to such extent that an illuminated sign over the doors once reading—"Fancy Automobile Company" will need to read—"Fancy Fruit Company" in order to depict more correctly the products for sale. And is there anyone today who cannot picture the delight on the faces of many automobile manufacturers of 1929 were they only in real business again at the old stand preparing fruits for needy markets?

The third principle of chemeconomics is stated as follows: *In an advancing civilization the prices of basic commodities must ever seek lower and lower levels in order that a greater and greater spread between this price and selling price of finished products may make possible an ever increasing expenditure for improvements.*

In order to keep the price levels on finished goods within reason the price levels on raw products must not increase appreciably on the basis of currency standard. This means that in periods of depression the price levels on raw products may remain stationary, but in periods of prosperity they must be lowered. By such procedure a greater and greater amount of labor can be employed on the production of finished goods.

In recent years the advent of the automobile

should have signified to the steel manufacturers that their products must be forced to the fore through constant improvements in same and lowering of selling prices. They followed a diametrically opposite course. The unnecessarily high priced automobile more than any one thing contributed to the credit smash and thus to the debacle of 1929. In the meantime the steel manufacturers have lost much of their former field to others who have learned how to advance chemically.

The fourth principle of chemeconomics is stated as follows: *With increasing income and education there is no upper limit to the capacity of man's wants.*

Leading manufacturers and agriculturists must be prepared to meet an ever growing competition from men of their own type and training. To keep abreast of this advance it becomes ever more necessary to offer new and more attractive finished products for human consumption.

New industries thus become the necessary adjuncts to an advancing civilization. In them must be absorbed the superfluous labor eliminated through steady advances in manufacturing technique. It is a backward organization that fails to accomplish the saving of as much as 5 per cent per annum in labor charges. It becomes imperative, therefore, that labor thus released shall be put into new industry, if we would escape periods of unrest as come upon us when unemployment exceeds one-third of the industrially employed. There can never be a dearth in new enterprise awaiting an enlightened people.

As the individual income increases the more will one expend on the amenities and luxuries of life; and as learning and skill are acquired, the more diversified and select will become these expenditures. All history teaches the impossibility of man ever being able to satiate man.

The fifth principle of chemeconomics is stated as follows: *All industry is basically chemical and hence industrial investments warrant constant chemico-physico-biological scrutiny.*

The man of today who would invest in an enterprise without knowledge of its financial standing is considered of weak mind. The man of tomorrow who would invest in an enterprise concerning which a constant scientific critique is unavailable will be known as a jackass.

The financial survey of an industrial organization is basic but not all embracive. Investment institutions, and individuals in general, will consult authorities of coordinated groups embracing the scientific scope of any or all industrial activities. For brevity we may call these consultants chemeconomists. Their findings can be revised overnight when and if the industrial organization under study departs from strictly scientific methods.

Without the backing and support of scientific authorities, no man's investments henceforth can carry any semblance to security as against the upheavals that are likely to come. The best of financial condition has been found altogether insufficient in many crises.

When chemeconomical considerations are made the basis of all industry and commerce then we shall have attained a normalcy that was foreordained by Nature. Those who rebel at such materialistic interpretations set themselves above Nature. Their Fate is known.

Foreign indebtedness to the United States has been the subject of much debate. Indeed those with no investments in general American manufacturers would have American factories close down pending the settlement of foreign debts by sale of goods to this country. They as yet have made no offer, either in public or private, to purchase the common stocks of all organizations directly to be affected by the type of goods to be imported!

Now chemically and physically one of the greatest sources of power is sunlight. It is necessary, however, that we have both sunlight and water for

many of the power schemes already proposed.
Future proposals will evolve from the old. This
has ever been the history of scientific discovery.
Upon such assumption the islands of the West
Indies are to become of greatest value to us.
They cannot become of such value to Great
Britain or to France. If, therefore, Great Britain
and France will sell us what we really need and
take in payment their cancelled indebtedness,
then the vexed problem can be settled overnight,
as it were, and all parties to the contracts will
become wealthier. To those malcontents who
argue we need not power, there is only one
answer—"Return to thy slumber."

The first suggestions to this end were made by
Lord Rothermere in 1919. The acreage involved
is trivial; but there seems to be a total incompre-
hension as to nationalistic demands. This arises
through lack of chemical and physical vision.
In the first place all of the inhabitants would need
to be removed within a reasonable time. For this
purpose they must be invited to emigrate to the
country of their choosing, with all moving expenses shared by the bargaining countries. In
other words, they are to retain their own nationali-
ties. Then again, as both France and Great
Britain desire naval bases in all parts of the
world, they should be allowed to retain their

present bases in the West Indies and about the Caribbean Sea and if they so wish, we could build them a few extra gratis.

The gist of the matter is that these islands are to become great chemical plants for our future. We should be able to bargain for them now upon amicable terms. Years hence when the urge on our part becomes acute, it may not be possible to strike such bargain for our future possessions. Why not improve the golden opportunity now? This is a beautiful example of chemeconomics in international affairs.

It is not to be expected that diplomats and statesmen can visualize chemical concepts; but at least they should be able to consider dispassionately the tremendous scientific trends at work in the domains of all nations. Naturally, all pernicious land-grabbing instincts within nations must be suppressed if reason, vision, and hope are to live.

CHAPTER XII

THE TRIUMPH

Modern civilization dates from the beginning of the nineteenth century. Little more than 100 years have come and gone to record in the world's history the most remarkable of all century periods.

A physico-consciousness acclaimed the birth of our civilization and a chemico-consciousness marks its present stage; they are guiding stars in human destiny.

The rise of these forces precipitated world-wide revolutions of such severity that life and labor became more arduous. It is as though these stars in their ascendency, drew all mankind to a higher plane of great complexities. Beyond each, and ever beckoning, is that goal of goals,—the revelation of man to himself and nature to man.

In the throes of revolutions it is natural that fear begets fear. The golden rays of light from our stars of destiny,—the emanations from these rising forces of revelation, oft seem dissipated. All this we attribute to improper dissemination of knowledge so lately acquired. Our activities remain the same but we are too often confused and perplexed. The basic activity of agriculture in particular exemplifies this state of uncertainty. When we realize fully the changes present and imminent there is no thought of fear,—rather indeed is it cheer.

But there are those who rebel at change. 'Tis they who decry research and would retard advance. They belong to a forgotten past. "The status of agriculture and mining," they cry, "grows steadily worse." Upon ancient standards, let such be granted. It is the present and future that claim our attention. To men of retrogressive mind, more than to all else, are we today indebted for the fruitless efforts towards relief to the toilers in industry.

No event of the past should ever deter human progress. We must study all in the light of science and command these findings to present endeavors. Madder was driven from cultivation simply by reason of a cheaper source of alizarin almost direct from anthracene, a by-product in coal tar. When a naturally occurring organic compound is of simple structure, as is alizarin, the changes generally favor its cheaper production through synthetic processes. Oil of wintergreen is an excellent example. Here is a compound, the methyl ester of salicyclic acid, obtainable from the low priced phenol through simple stages. The natural source,—wintergreen berry, is obtainable in low yield per acre and affords no known by-product. Little if any hope can ever be entertained toward a return of such to agriculture.

On the other hand, the oil of peppermint is of composite type, containing a number of valuable components. Synthesis of any one or all is not simple and hence the likelihood of replacement of peppermint cultivation by a synthetic substitute far removed. Furthermore the plant lends itself to intensive cultivation. Its future, however, is bound up in the demand for menthol, one of its components.

No more severe stroke to agriculture is recorded than the replacement of cotton, in increasing measure, by a high grade α-cellulose prepared from wood through chemical agencies; it is the same in effect had the chemist synthesized cotton itself at low cost. Many years will pass ere the final curtain is drawn on the cotton fields and possibly by that time a new species of cellulose linter producing plants will have been introduced to cultivation.

The repression of cultivation of natural indigo was brought about by the inability on the part of the growers to supply the dye at a price commensurate with the synthetic product. At that stage in agriculture (1897) nothing otherwise could have been expected. Today we can grow a better plant in Natal, hardier and heavier of leaf, that is richer in coloring matter, than was grown in Behar (India). In olden days these leaves (40 per cent of total plant) yielded about 0.5 per cent of coloring matter (0.2 per cent on total plant), today we are assured of a yield of 0.7 per cent. Even this larger yield is possible of increase. But until there comes a demand for some of the by-products (such as indirubin) or for other parts of the plant itself, it is not likely to come back into cultivation. If, however, the price of synthetic indigo were to rise, we might well expect a return to natural indigo. As a matter of chemical insight, we know now that the cost of synthetic indigo will drop.

It is a new order in agriculture that faces us. This order calls for carbohydrates (cellulose, starch, and sugars) and vegetable oils and proteins as the basic output. A number of these compounds have been synthesized but only at high cost, owing to complexity of reactions. Their continued supply is far better attainable through agricultural efforts.

In the building up of sugars through condensation of formaldehyde which in turn arises by the action of light, catalyzed by chlorophyll, upon carbon dioxide and water, there is tremendous advantage on the side of nature. The slowness of the reaction militates, for the time being, against any commercial application. When sugars can be secured direct from nature, or through simple hydrolytic steps (as is glucose from starch), and at a price between 1 and 2 cents per pound, we need not look further. In the same manner cellulose (of long chain structure and with units like to sugar) even though capable of biochemical synthesis from sugars, is best obtained direct from nature.

Vegetable oils can be synthesized from simpler carbon compounds but here likewise the possibility of any low priced finished product is far removed. Such oils through esterification and hydrogenation are abundantly able to supply the demands for fats.

The great field of proteins, such as meats and the like, remains for future resolution. The basic compounds here concerned are the aliphatic amino acids. The synthesis of proteins is possible but not likely to attain any degree of synthetic production for many years. That such day is approaching there remains no doubt. Its arrival will be the signal for removal of the remains of dead animals from our table. This transformation is comprehended under the biologico-genesis already discussed.

It is the adaptation of the soil in nature's great laboratory to processing in general that offers unlimited possibilities for the immediate future. In the manufacturing plant we are limited as to area, installation, and labor. The more closely the factory approaches the processes of nature, the more likely will be its economic stability. Throughout our modern world these two agencies must ever be held in balance.

Far more striking to the layman is the realization that scientific knowledge gained in nature's laboratory is under constant transmission through countless channels into every walk of life; there to constitute a greater and greater governing factor in man's pursuits. After all this is exactly in the nature of things. Man is an assistant to nature in nature's laboratory and never can thwart nature's plan. His life must be chemeconomically in tune with nature.

There are, nevertheless, many who honestly believe that since nature's workshop is just the same worskshop as of yore, then fathers' ways should be good enough for today. Of all so minded, let us ask, "what has happened to man?" Let us look upon this man from nature's standpoint.

For millions and millions of years the forces of nature have been constantly at work manufacturing, resolving, decomposing, preserving, and yet remanufacturing hundreds of thousands of compounds in one vast superfluity. The earth had come to a sort of equilibrium chemogenetically speaking, when along came man. A million years or more passed before this man made the slightest use of reserved stores. His life was just a replica of other wild animals,—eating and being eaten in turn.

Now when agriculture was begun we discern the first instance of man's dabbling in this great chemical laboratory of nature. Of course, he understood nothing of what he was about, save that he could increase his worldly goods by growing foods in this laboratory. Thousands of years passed and the knowledge accumulated by his predecessors became actually serviceable on demand for his own experimentations. This is to say, he finally evolved a laboratory manual.

Prior to the advent of this laboratory manual, which is, of course, coincident with the appearance of printed books, the intelligent man was really more concerned in giving up the laboratory. Various religious cults from early times had been prophesying a future when man was to have wings and nothing to do but fly around through a maze of golden avenues. Even though inherently of good moral instincts, it was nevertheless required of man that he devote a lot of time in preparing himself for the coming metamorphosis. The fund required for such preparatory training was merely easy money for the promoters; but the idea after all so appealed to the vanity of man that years of backwardness resulted. Of course, his laboratory work suffered frightfully.

But after a time certain outstanding discoveries by noted students revealed the intricate wonders of this great laboratory in which he dwelt. Man betook himself everywhere to a closer study of nature. Discovery after discovery unfolded itself to him. And then, he came upon the steam engine; slowly but surely he now had something to speed his work and his travel. The wings of religious promise lost interest. Through the turmoils of that great mechanical revolution he awoke to a realization that he was master of all he surveyed.

Upon introspection man soon realized his own shortcomings. The very substance of all things around him was totally incomprehensible to him. He delved further and further into chemical experiments. Nature was good to him and gradually took him into closer confidence. She tutored him in the use of her tools. She showed him the inner structure of molecular arrangements. Little by little he learned to unravel the many intricacies of her delicate workmanship; and how simple everything appeared. Diligently man applied himself to duplicating some of nature's work by striking off at new angles. In many cases, as he thought, he came upon simpler processes than were nature's. He was enraptured.

It was not enough that man should be in physical control of the world at his feet. He gained chemical control likewise of the air above him; a discovery that led to terrible war and frightful devastation. But man is pressing on. Nature opens more and more of the doors to inner secrets. She bids him be not afraid—there is vastly more than he can ever comprehend.

A study of these intricate mechanisms of nature reveals ever a simplicity beyond belief. Water, oxygen, carbon dioxide, and ammonia, in the presence of salts, constitute the gamut of her reactants. Her four generally known agencies are heat, light, electricity, and pressure. Whether in direct syntheses of compounds or through intervening agencies of microörganisms, the drift is ever toward greater complexities. It is here that nature has need of intelligent man to assist in raising still higher the plane of civilization. Endless are the possibilities and entrancing beyond words the hopes of origination.

It is the cry of the old frontier. That wanderlust that carried man to the corners of the earth and at last fell dormant with no more lands to conquer. The intellectual horizon is now broadening and advancing over fields of unknown beauty. Rapture and delight in the fulness of knowledge hold forth their enticements. A new urge arises; the old-time wanderlust of the rough and ready days gives way to a *wissenlust*,—a thirst for knowledge. This is the urge that neither can be assuaged nor abated.

At last the awakening—the triumph of man in a chemical world. Everything his heart can desire, all manner of novelties his imagination can picture, lie in the powers of his master. He must work with nature hand in hand that they together may turn all to the good of mankind. Thus is dawning the greatest era of happiness and prosperity.

It matters not what man has accomplished in his own little way. He has only been practicing, or drilling himself in the use of nature's tools. When he learns more of nature's methods that are surpassingly wonderful and rich in promise, he will apply them in the great laboratory that is his. Amply sufficient is the capacity of this laboratory for the supply of foods and necessities of life to all the inhabitants of earth for millions of years to come.

Thus is chemistry triumphant. To scientists in general it is the unfolding of nature's forces, but to the chemist it is the atonement so long awaited, when nature and man could effect that which only nature heretofore controlled. In the Divine plan this stage must have been predestined. Today we are at its threshold. Tomorrow a new life begins.

OTHER TITLES IN A CENTURY OF PROGRESS SERIES

FRONTIERS OF MEDICINE *(Medicine)*
    MORRIS FISHBEIN, Editor of Journal of American Medical
    Association
OUR MINERAL CIVILIZATION *(Mining and Metallurgical*
Engineering)
    THOMAS T. READ, School of Mines, Columbia University, New
    York City
ALL ABOUT OIL *(Petroleum)*
    GUSTAV EGLOFF, Universal Oil Products Company, Chicago,
    Illinois
TIME, SPACE, AND ATOMS *(Physics)*
    RICHARD T. COX, Department of Physics, New York University,
    University Heights, N. Y.
ADJUSTMENT AND MASTERY *(Psychology)*
    ROBERT S. WOODWORTH, Department of Psychology, Columbia
    University, New York City

Sans Tache

Sans Tache

IN THE "elder days of art" each artist or craftsman enjoyed the privilege of independent creation. He carried through a process of manufacture from beginning to end. The scribe of the days before the printing press was such a craftsman. So was the printer in the days before the machine process. He stood or fell, as a craftsman, by the merit or demerit of his finished product.

Modern machine production has added much to the worker's productivity and to his material welfare; but it has deprived him of the old creative distinctiveness. His work is merged in the work of the team, and lost sight of as something representing him and his personality.

Many hands and minds contribute to the manufacture of a book, in this day of specialization. There are seven distinct major processes in the making of a book: The type must first be set; by the monotype method, there are two processes, the "keyboarding" of the MS and the casting of the type from the perforated paper rolls thus produced. Formulas and other intricate work must be hand-set; then the whole brought together ("composed") in its true order, made into pages and forms. The results must be checked by proof reading at each stage. Then comes the "make-ready" and press-run and finally the binding into volumes.

All of these processes, except that of binding into cloth or leather covers, are carried on under our roof.

The motto of the Waverly Press is *Sans Tache*. Our ideal is to manufacture books *"without blemish"*—worthy books, worthily printed, with worthy typography—books to which we shall be proud to attach our imprint, made by craftsmen who are willing to accept open responsibility for their work, and who are entitled to credit for creditable performance.

The printing craftsman of today is quite as much a craftsman as his predecessor. There is quite as much discrimination between poor work and good. We are of the opinion that the individuality of the worker should not be wholly lost. The members of our staff who have contributed their skill of hand and brain to this volume are:

Keyboard: Vera Taylor.

Casters: Charles Aher, Ernest Wann, Kenneth Brown, Mahlon Robinson, Martin Griffen, George Bullinger, Charles Fick, Norwood Eaton, Henry Lee, George Smith.

Composing Room: John Crabill, Robert Daily, John Flanagan, James Jackson, Robert Lambert, Emerson Madairy, Anthony Wagner, Edward Rice, Richard King, Henry Shea, George Moss, Theodore Nilson, Henry Johansen.

Proof Room: Alice Reuter, Mary Reed, Ruth Jones, Shirley Seidel, Audrey Knight, Dorothy Fick, Betty Williams, Alice Grabau, Catharine Dudley, Louisa Westcott, Virginia Williams, Roland Orth, Evelyn Rogers.

Press: Hugh Gardner, Henry Augsburg, Henry Hager.

Folders: Laurence Krug, Clifton Hedley.

Cutter: William Armiger.